THAT NICE MISS SMITH

by

NIGEL MORLAND

St. Martin's Press
New York

Library of Congress Cataloging-in-Publication Data

Morland, Nigel.
    That nice Miss Smith / Nigel Morland.
        p.   cm.
    "A Thomas Dunne book."
    ISBN 0-312-03439-3
        1. Poisoning—Scotland—History—19th century—Case studies.
2. Smith, Madeleine Hamilton, 1835-1928.   3. Poisoners—Scotland
—Biography.   I. Title.
    HV6555.G72S365 1989
    364.1'523'092—dc20
    [B]   89-34939
                                                            CIP

First published in Great Britain by Souvenir Press Ltd.

First U.S. Edition

10 9 8 7 6 5 4 3 2 1

for
Mother

Contents

Illustrations

Acknowledgments

It is right I should thank a number of people for helping me, first being James H. McKechnie, who presented me with a trunk filled with miscellanea collected by his grandfather, an ardent Smith fan. It was a treasure-chest of literary gold.

There is Thomas Langlois, an old man with an excellent memory, who knew Elmire Langelier and gave me, from notes and memory, much of the family background.

Similar in his provision of notes and facts was James Mackenzie, of Falkirk, whose associations with the Smith family were intimate.

In Jersey I must first make special note of my gratitude to my mother, Mrs. G. A. Lomax, and to Father H. Verkin, Miss Sormany, and Raymond Falle, and this goes, too, for my London agent, Miss Christine Campbell Thomson, who nursed this book to life.

Others I should like to mention are George Wilton Wilton; W. N. Roughead; James H. Hodge (for much advice and certain useful photographs); Mrs. Edith M. Faulstich, of New York, whose research work was invaluable; Bernard Darwin; James Negus; A. Irvine Adams; John H. Scholes, of the British Transport Commission; J. H. Alexander, of Dicksons & Co., the Registrar General of Scotland; the Librarians of the Signet Library, the National Library of Scotland, the Mitchell Library, the Dundee and Buckinghamshire Public Libraries.

I would like to thank Mrs. Roger Fullerton and Mrs. J. H. Manning for many personal facts, and Lilian Stow, whose great-uncle conducted a lively correspondence with Mrs. Gorton at Clapton. One of his letters contained a note from a lady who saw Madeleine at the ball in Govan village: "She

xi

was a bonny young woman, bright of eye, and beautiful of complexion. Her carriage was excellent and I found her quite charming, with such a pure speaking voice . . . in repose she seemed sad . . . but such a fetching personality."

I have relied on many letters, trivia, and diaries for my background, after authenticating them, and this means numerous helpful people have been left out here and abroad, as well as several specialists in medical jurisprudence, forensic chemistry, and men of law who wish to remain anonymous.

It would be discourteous of me not to thank people who made my stay in Scotland so pleasant by their kindness, among them Sir Compton Mackenzie; Moray McLaren; John R. Jamieson and his family; Mr. and Mrs. James H. Hodge; Dr. and Mrs. J. Menzies Campbell; Dr. Alistair Mair; T. J. N. Smyth; D. J. Stevenson, and, in particular, Miss Winifred Duke.

And to Miss Fryn Tennyson Jesse my grateful thanks for her enormous enthusiasm about Madeleine, her willing help and guidance.

NIGEL MORLAND

Preface

Considering the circumstances of my first meeting with Nigel Morland, I find it hard to explain why I did not determine, there and then, that it should also be the last. It was on a summer's day of the early 1970s; if I needed to, I could fix the exact date, for the temperature, strangely for England, was over 90. Hearing that I was in Brighton, doing research into the epidemic of 'trunk crimes' that had beset that town nearly forty years before, he had phoned me, saying that he had information about one of the 'trunk criminals', and inviting me for tea at his home near Bognor Regis, about fifteen miles west along the south coast from Brighton. I drove there.

His house, a bungalow, was at the edge of a beach of yellow sand. I knocked — several times — but there was no answer. As 'tea' is such an imprecise term, with meanings ranging from a mere cup of tea to an afternoon feast, I had gone without lunch. And so I was hungry — and, because of the awful heat, even more thirsty. There were several refreshment vans nearby, each chiming a different happy tune but none selling anything other than American fizzy drinks, ice-lollies, and peculiarly-flavoured potato crisps. I paced up and down outside the house — soon tiredly, because the drifted sand was inches deep in the facing lane, and almost as soon petulantly. After ten minutes which seemed like as many hours, a small elderly man, dapper in a three-piece suit and carrying an umbrella, appeared at the landward end of the lane; walking faster than most men can run, he headed for the house where I had been invited for tea. I guessed that he was Nigel Morland. He, having guessed who I was, snapped, 'A mite inconvenient, your coming today,' as he

xiii

flashed past me. Assuming that I was meant to, I followed him into the house. He told me to go into the front room as he disappeared into a back one. The front room was, in one respect, a sort of addendum to the beach: every stick of furniture was covered with sand, deep enough in certain crannies for the flourishing of sea-grass, the carpet went crunch when I walked on it, sand was triangled in corners, the fireplace was like a dune. It occurred to me that the house, which was called Seaspray, should have been called Sandstorm. I wondered where Morland kept his typewriter, and how he kept it unclogged with sand.

He soon reappeared, smelling of Old Spice. He was wearing a different three-piece suit. He explained — but did not apologise for the fact — that he had to get back to the Conservative Club in Bognor: to a meeting of some sort that he, as chairman of it, had adjourned for half an hour, having suddenly remembered that he had invited me for tea. He asked me which way I would be driving back to Brighton. I told him my intended route, which went no-where nearer to Bognor than where I was parked, and he said that in that case he would prevail upon me to make 'a very slight detour' so as to drop him back at the Conservative Club. As I drove there — going by his directions, which took me the wrong way along one-way streets — he waved to practically every pedestrian we passed; they all waved back, and some of those whom he hadn't waved to waved to him. I felt rather as the Queen Mother's chauffeur must feel. He chattered throughout the journey — about, among other persons, Edward Heath, Charles Peace, the Reverend Ian Paisley, and, for no more than a few seconds, the 'trunk criminal' I had expected to spend the whole afternoon talking about — and, prior to scampering up the steps to the club, said, 'You must come for tea some other time. I've so enjoyed meeting you. Bye-bye. Oh blow, I've left my brolly at home. Can't be helped. Bye-bye.' On my way out of the town, I got a puncture. While changing the wheel, I thought of King George V's comment during a discussion as to where

he should be taken for a convalescence: 'Bugger Bognor.' I
added Nigel Morland's name to that of the place.

But gradually, over the next year or so, I became one of
his many friends. Our friendship lasted till he died, aged
eighty, in the spring of 1986.

His arranging of our first meeting for a time when he was
supposed to be somewhere else can be tagged to a mass of
stronger evidence that he could not resist doing more than
too many things concurrently. I don't think I have ever
known anyone quite so diversely busy. And I have certainly
never known anyone who claimed to have come across so
many people who, seemingly ordinary then, had turned out
to be extraordinary. The very tallness of some of those tales
made it hard to believe that he had invented them. While still
in rompers, he had, so he said, been dandled by Dr Crippen
— while working as a reporter in Shanghai, he had, so he
said, saved the young Mao Tse-tung from being murdered
by a mob of Emperor-supporters — soon after the Second
World War, he had, so he said, been in a pub in High Street
Kensington at the same time as Neville Heath (who subsequently committed two murders), John George Haigh (who
was midway though a spate of murders, though perhaps not
yet using an acid-bath for the disposal of his victims), and a
comparatively inoffensive criminal known as The Mad
Major.

There is no doubt that he did spend a year of the 1920s in
Shanghai — and that, when he returned home, Edgar
Wallace, a friend of his mother's, encouraged him to write
fiction and helped him to get it accepted. Over the following
half-century, he published at least 200 novels — many of
them pseudonymously (as, for instance, Norman Forrest,
Neal Shepherd, Mary Dane), most of them to do with crime,
and some of those having the same detecting character, Mrs
Palmyra Pym, a sort of uncelibate Jane Marple. Meanwhile, he wrote innumerable short stories and bits of journ-
alism, edited the *Edgar Wallace Mystery Magazine*, and
somehow found the time, the energy, for heaven knows how

many extra-literary activities. In 1953 he and the even more prolific novelist John Creasey (not yet singularly entranced by his notion of a non-party political party) founded the Crime Writers' Association.

A dozen years later, he and Edgar Wallace's son-in-law set up a publishing firm, the Tallis Press, the main outcome of which was a quasi-quarterly journal devoted to true crime, which he edited; starting off as *Crime & Detection* but soon re-christened *The Criminologist*, it was a ragbag of contributions, some excellent, some just OK, and one (which, never minding absence of evidence, dragged the Royal Family into the Name-the-Ripper game) sly and sleazy.

Nigel Morland wrote only a few true-crime books. The best of them — far and away the best — are the two monographs on famous poisoning cases: *That Friendless Lady*, dealing with the Maybrick case, and *this* one, which is not only the better of the two but also the best of the several books, each by a different author, on the Madeleine Smith case. I am glad that it is back in print. It deserves to be.

JONATHAN GOODMAN

THAT NICE MISS SMITH

CHAPTER ONE

Jersey Panorama

Of Pierre Emile L'Angelier's antecedents very little is known.

Peter Hunt: *The Madeleine Smith Affair.*

LACE CURTAINS FLUTTERED gently under the touch of questing fingers; within they waited anxiously for news.

From the discreet mansions of Charlotte Square—secure in the beauty endowed by the Adam Brothers—down through the social strata to the Water of Leith, Edinburgh was tense and expectant.

The elegant ladies who had just risen from luncheon and the poor whose dinners had been taken on bare table-tops talked of one thing—the charitable wondered about that nice Miss Smith, in whose guilt they could not believe, just as the ungenerous thought in less kindly channels.

In that Scottish city, where the tail end of June's heat-wave still lingered, they had almost forgotten far-off Lucknow and Delhi, where the beleaguered garrisons still held out against the rising tide of mutineers. Nothing seemed to matter except the remarkable trial in the High Court of Justiciary.

On that day in 1857 the whole country's eyes were also on the justice place, for this was to be the hour of decision.

What the reckoning was to be remained any man's guess. Every rumour was an answer, yet never the real one. The jury's verdict had still to settle tidily and for ever the problem of those star-crossed lovers.

Then the lace curtains fluttered again. In the busy streets sounded, like gull-cries above the Firth of Forth, the calls of racing news-boys, fraught with excitement . . .

*   *   *

1

The island was small, no more than a pebble in a group of pebbles clinging to the coast of France. But the island wanted no part of its mother. When she had threatened, the men of the island stood to arms. Each citizen was a soldier in embryo, waiting willingly to watch the twisting coastline that the monster did not set forth to bring Jersey once more under the thrall of Normandy, a separation seven hundred years old.

In those days it was a quaint, virtually unknown land, a Jersey owing allegiance to England, yet a self-contained microcosm bitterly independent of other lands.

The capital, St. Helier, was a town of a thousand houses, governing centre of a population barely half its modern total.

Before the Eagle, the all-conquering Napoleon, had been pinioned, there was a temporary prosperity. The English government had reinforced its military to fortify this foremost bastion against him.

The primitive island roads ("some of the worst in Europe") were soon intersected with good highways built to facilitate the movement of troops. Money spent by the big garrison went to swell the tangle of French and Spanish coinage which was the local currency.

War stepped up the island's chief export of cider, while the soldiery got drunk on the unpleasant cider brew for which St. Helier was infamous. On the quays the loads of cows and fruits were increased for dispatch to England's open arms.

By 1820 the Napoleonic terror was becoming a memory. The English tide had receded, leaving numbers behind who had found the island something they could not abandon, though for years, except in matters of trade, there was little intermingling of newcomers and natives.

Prosperity, if it had not gone, was less than in days of war, a change more obvious in the centres of fashion and among the transients than in the island's entrenched, much intermarried families.

Their ways were largely unchanged. They talked in their

Jersey-French vernacular, or in the good French of the governing circles. In the countryside the urban patois was the general rule.

Yet the English had left their mark. Their tongue was more frequently heard, now they had brought Jersey from its centuries of almost complete isolation. The schools taught the alien language, and, despite a flood of immigrants from France, the English were growing more numerous. Living was cheap.

The Jersiais got along with them in the manner common to many lands on which the amiable regiments have descended. The King's money was wholly acceptable, and some of the shops were now installing new fronts and changing from oil- to gas-illumination, but in the streets at night the bobbing lanterns carried by pedestrians were still to be seen.

* * *

It was with the English in mind that Pierre Jean Langelier had thought of a practical marriage.

Born in Mesnil Boeufs, Normandy, Pierre and his brother, René, had left France in 1813 to settle in peaceful Jersey away from the French monarchy with which, as republican-minded men, they did not sympathise. They were nurserymen with a small market-garden in St. Saviour's Road.

Pierre at twenty-six was a hard-working man whose shrewd brown eyes had watched the growth of gentlemen's fine walled houses along his road. He had learned of the excellent trade done by his friends at the markets of St. Helier.

A few doors from his own holding, on the same east side of the road, was the family of de la Croix. They had come from Daivainel, Somme, to work in Jersey as merchants. Claude Marie and Marguerite de la Croix were estimable, and sound in tradition. Their children were brought up in the customary Jersey ways.

It was on the eldest daughter, Victoire Melanie, that Pierre had fixed his attention. She was no beauty, but a sensible girl adept in the manner of her day at all household crafts.

She and Pierre were finally married in July, 1822, at the Chapel of St. Louis in St. Helier in the family presence, with Melanie's friend, Cécile Mauny, there to lend her support.

After the marriage the pair were poor. They had sunk their money—his savings and her *dot*—in a little seed shop they opened in the Rue des Vignes, behind the Rue de Derrière.

They imported seeds from England to supply to the new gentry, and sold at as much as five guineas a hundred the giant *Chaumontelle* pears, which René grew, and the fashionable gift for visitors to send home.

The old town was developing now, and changing. Few of the country farmers were to be seen in their cocked hats and queues *a la française* or their wives in short jackets and red flannel petticoats. "Abandoned females" on street corners at night were a growing problem, but at least Napoleon was really dead and buried.

On April 30, 1823, the first little Langelier was born. This was Pierre Emile; grandfather and grandmother Claude and Marguerite de la Croix were godparents at the christening.

*   *   *

Pierre now possessed a son to inherit his humble seed shop though, under the Jersey system of *gavel-kind** the boisterous, brown-eyed baby's chances for the future looked less and less hopeful when the indefatigable Melanie produced Anastasie Melanie in June, 1824; Achille Jean in May, two years later, and weakly Zephirine Melanie on March 26, 1829. The last of the brood was to be Elmire Jeanne, who was not born till January, 1834.

The seed shop's living-quarters were not only full but overcrowded.

A new shop was sought in the vicinity at 8 Library Place. Being close to the chief church and adjacent to La Place Royale, the centre of government, it was to be hoped the

---

* Equal division of the family fortune among the body heirs with actual property going to the eldest son.

English would more frequently patronise the *maison* Langelier.

Little Emile was a charming boy. Knowing he was the eldest, he was properly conscious of his importance, the family right of all the eldest sons in the island.

He was to learn that highway robbery and burglary were still punishable with death. These things he accepted along with the ruder customs of the times.

The heavy Jersey box carts, drawn by unkempt horses, daily threatened his life in the narrow streets where every chimney smoked alarmingly, and where no permanent Catholic Church had yet been built.

He had the excitement of market-day on Saturdays, when relatives and friends came slowly in from the country. The garrison troops or the local militia were always there to fill him with martial ardour, and, inherited from France, numerous festivals and celebratory days to be enjoyed. For a small boy it was a decent, peaceful life, with less family regimentation than would have been the case in England.

When he was enrolled at the National School, he was put with some four hundred children to absorb a sound if elementary tuition. It was in the English tongue he was to acquire fluency until he was as proficient in it as he was in the French of the family hearth. His ear was good and he was to lose every trace of his accent until his was almost the diction of a born Englishman.

In other things his aptitude for learning was mediocre. He acquired the rudiments of education but did not shine in any subject. At least he learned enough to help his father in the shop; a paid assistant was beyond the family purse.

* * *

Bright, gay, a little vain but always kind and properly filial, Emile developed into a pleasant youth with signs of coming good looks. His young sister enjoyed his company; he dutifully did his share in looking after Achille and tiny Elmire, in the fashion common to families of French descent.

But in this descent he was entirely disinterested. He was, from childhood, a Jersiais—proud, insular, and devoted to his island soil.

His world was a happy, self-contained place where the family was the centre of all things and his mother its guiding hand. But she, with a clear eye on the future, saw for him insufficient to his advantage on the island when he grew up. She constantly drew his attention to England, to the big island where the frenzied clatter of the accelerating mechanical age had taken over the direction of life. In one thing Emile was fortunate—he was born in an era, in the half-century, when the greatest changes came, changes unequalled in any other phase of history.

That was for the future. At present there remained the circumscribed routine of daily existence.

The move to Library Place had done the seed shop a certain amount of good. It was at least fully paid for by Pierre's sale of his share of the nursery business in St. Saviour's Road. He received money both for the good-will and half the value of the land, reckoned then at £76 the *vergée* (2¼ Jersey *vergées* go to one English acre).

Emile's transition from childhood was that of any normal boy. With growing awareness he got to understand something of the world about him. There were the usual juvenile flirtations both harmless and discreet, if, on the feminine side, conducted with some vehemence; he was growing quite good-looking and, according to the usual old wives, would be a heart-breaker one day.

At home Melanie always wanted him to consider the time when he must take over the family business—when school was ended he had to keep this in mind. He had three sisters whose portions it would probably be his duty to provide. Achille was only a young boy and not for years could he be a useful member of the family.

Pierre was not at all well at that time. It was nothing of real consequence, yet his indifferent health worried him as he toiled away in the shop in his frock coat, tight trousers, and the inevitable dark velvet waistcoat crossed by a sturdy Breton watch-chain. The shopman's apron was not for Pierre; his instinct was that seeds and flowers were gentlemanly and to sell them to the gentry he dressed in a civilised fashion.

* * *

There was a flourishing nursery not far from the Langelier holding, owned by an Englishman named Saunders.

In the courteous island custom, where trade rivalries were superficial rather than real, Saunders had at times occasion to call at Library Place. Perhaps he liked the gay Langelier family, or, more probably in the manner of many local people, he admired the hard-working wife whose reputation and family were of the best in merchant circles.

It was to him Melanie later addressed her wish for Emile to learn something to ground him for his future responsibilities. The English were so evidently the people with whom to do business. In order to please them it was necessary for someone one day to replace dear Papa's distinct French accent and Norman narrowness with a wider outlook and experience.

Saunders was moved to suggest that Emile might be apprenticed to him. In his nursery, laid out on modern lines, was everything a young man could learn in dealing with the growing annual influx of visitors.

Family consultations took place about the step. Pierre listened to the views of his de la Croix in-laws as both better informed than he was and supported by the knowledge he lacked.

In the end Emile went to Saunders' nursery with indentures for five years. It was at first strange and foreign. English was spoken all the time (the prevailing prices did not appeal to the thrifty Jersiais), and foreign customers were the rule.

Emile was happy. He was learning a comprehensive business, and acquiring an international point of view. He was to go through every department, and did so willingly. His work was good and his intelligence high. Male customers liked his courtesy, the women his charm and looks.

In 1840 tragedy struck. Pierre Langelier died. The cause of death does not seem clear, but his life had been a hard one and years of open-air work had done him no more good than the constant worry of the seed shop. One existing letter indicates it was a chill aggravated by inattention—most likely pneumonia developed.

There was a funeral with the customary Jersey procession to Green Street Cemetery, strongly attended by mourners— from grown-ups to babies in arms—wearing elaborate, un-relieved sable clothing.

Melanie was prostrate. Not only was she a widow but she had to cope with the many problems of the shop, and care for her family. She did not wish to break Emile's indentures, nor did he desire to enter into his rights as inheritor of the property; he wished his mother to retain it, and so it was arranged. Achille was still a schoolboy, Zephirine only eleven and Elmire just six. Her real assistant was sixteen-year-old Anastasie.*

Without Pierre's shrewd trading and buying experience, the business barely managed to give them more than a meagre living. Then, two years later, Emile's charm was responsible for the next happening. A chance visitor to the island called at Saunders' nursery.

He was a dignified, heavily-built Scotsman of early middle age whose estates were near Conanbridge, at the foot of Cromarty Firth in Ross-shire. This was Sir Francis Mackenzie, Bt., of Gairloch, who was waited on by Emile when making his purchases. It was a brief visit which extended to over an hour.

There were other calls at the nursery by Sir Francis. He took an instant liking to the slight, dark-haired, nineteen-year-old Emile. It was a liking inspired by the Scots'

* Much confusion prevails in every other book on the Madeleine Smith case here; Madame Langelier carried on the business entirely alone until her death. After that Anastasie took over, a distant relative coming in to help. When Anastasie died, he married Elmire.

affinity with the Gallic temperament. Where Sir Francis was almost dour, Emile was volatile and excitable. He possessed neither his father's Norman caution nor the native Jersey sobriety. Perhaps it was inherited from some Gascon ancestor, for there was a lot of the traditional Gascon about Emile in his adult years.

Sir Francis wished to take him back to Scotland in his service at the Conanbridge estate. It was a form of patronage bestowed on promising youths by the aristocracy, a dying custom left over from the days of the Georges.

It was a surprising idea, more so to Saunders than to Melanie. She saw its advantages. The wealthy stranger assured her Emile would not only be adequately paid, but would (which was Emile's expressed desire) be able to send home a regular sum.

There was again a family council, with the de la Croix in the dominant role. It was a letter, still in existence, from Cécile Mauny which influenced Claude, in his dual capacity of grandfather and godfather, to see that Emile would be safe with "the Scotch," for "Sir Mackenzie must indeed be an English duke." It settled the problem in the sensible French way, swayed by, but indifferent to, the exactitudes of nobility, or race.

Saunders readily gave back to Emile his indentures, and Sir Francis, in expressing his delight, was nervous that the icy heaths of Conan House would be too overwhelming for a young man brought up in the temperate Jersey air. He planned to make the change slowly by putting his charge for a year with the highly respectable firm of Dicksons and Company, Edinburgh nurserymen, from whom he was a buyer of great quantities of forest trees.

The Langelier shop was in a state of excitement when leave-taking arrived. The recent funeral of two years back was still indicated by partial mourning, but a new relative was present in the form of cousin Edouard Langelier, who had recently arrived from St. Jouan des Guérets with his affianced and her family. They were soon to be married in

St. Helier and an invitation to the whole family had eased the distress of the parting.

Cécile Mauny is again the authority for pictures of the prevailing uproar, and the visits by every remote relative and friend on the island.

Emile was to make the crossing to Southampton on the eighteen-hour journey of the regular packet. For this had been paid the large sum of a guinea. He would then proceed by train, unknown in Jersey. Sir Francis had paid for everything, including a new suit of clothes and a leather hamper. Melanie had little to give, but she and the girls saw to it that skilled needlework supplied everything in the way of shirts and haberdashery.

It was like a journey to the ends of the earth. They could only imagine Scotland, believed to be a wilderness of ice and snow, which, the gossips announced, caused the breath to freeze.

*   *   *

It was as if Emile Langelier's evil star took over his destiny once he had set foot in Edinburgh, where his adult life was to begin and where its epitaph would be written fifteen years later.

A trifle scared of this new world, and somewhat bold and boastful to counteract his inner fears, he tried to conform to northern standards in a town where the winds were harsh compared with home, and the people quiet and shyly distant.

He missed the warm, uninhibited affection of Library Place, nor could he understand the Scots. They gave him kindness but did not smile easily. One or two letters to his mother—baldly uninformative as they were—fail to conceal his uneasy feelings. Without being properly equipped for it, the sudden change was too much for his spiritual equilibrium.

The following year, in June, 1843, Sir Francis Mackenzie, on a visit to London, was laid low with an apoplectic seizure. Within minutes of the stroke he was dead.

Emile, nearly six hundred impassable miles from Jersey, was entirely alone and without resources.

CHAPTER TWO

Maiden in Waiting

*. . . that tropical and gorgeous flower so astoundingly out
of due season put forth by a decent family tree, in the
uncongenial soil of mid-Victorian Glasgow.*
William Roughead: *Malice Domestic.*

DEMURE IN HER brown, tight-bodiced dress, she stood there
in the dull mid-morning light. Her bonnet had a shallow
crown and its ribbon, tied into a large bow over her throat,
gave her a childish charm.

In the hurrying crowds of Glasgow's Bridge Street terminus
she was an island of placidity, ignoring the authoritative
blowings of the engine, intent only on the business of farewell.

Papa was beside her, splendid in dark clothes and the full
whiskers he adopted three years before the necessities of the
Crimea made them fashionable. Mama was of course flus-
tered; she invariably was, and had checked the valise, the
two bags, and the straw hold-all at least several times.

For Madeleine Hamilton Smith London was an impending
adventure, and Mrs. Gorton's school a novelty.

But she did not show it. Her large grey eyes were impassive
and her gloved hands still—that stillness was always to be
her paramount quality.

Only when warnings of imminent departure sounded did
she become animated. Her latent appeal was suddenly manifest with what moderns would dub sex-appeal. It seemed to
turn on as if by a switch immediately she moved or spoke.

The last good-byes were said and she was safely settled at
the side of Mrs. McIntosh in the dark-green coach. This
friend of Mama's was to see her to London, and, though
otherwise unknown, has left a long letter, signed "Janie

11

McIntosh," which pictures the departure and the journey. Written a few years later, even allowing for the inaccuracies or exaggerations of memory, hers seems a good recollection.

The engine drew the train from the station. The two women travellers were to stay the night with friends when they reached Carlisle Citadel Joint Station, prior to venturing on the morrow's eight-hour run to Euston.

In the meantime there was the strangeness of it all to enjoy, in the comfortable three-a-side compartment where, that winter afternoon, the dim pot-lamps above would shed their ghostly light. For Madeleine it was a considerable change from her uneventful, conventional life.

She was not a beautiful girl in that little bonnet which apparently achieved the desired effect of "a wind-blown rose held upside down." Her face was too long, her features too small, and her nose too obvious. Nor was her mouth good, but her hair, nearly hidden though it was, shone bright and dark above her wide eyes.

Of average height in shoes, and "alluringly proportioned," with a full, high bust and "excellent movement," she was apt to be made insignificant by her quality of stillness.

It was unusual how her appeal drew men in those moments of animation, even when she was a young girl. Yet on entering a room where she was sitting, they never seemed to notice her, at first.

Before she could associate with the male world there was school. It had been Papa's notion she should "finish" in London.* His Glasgow friends thought it an odd whim. Scotland had places where she might have gone, or, as some of the travelled ones suggested, there was France or even Switzerland.

This did not do for James Smith, and Mrs. Gorton's Academy for Young Ladies was his final choice. There had been excellent reports of it, and, which appealed to him, it was both sound and reasonable. As a successful architect

* Her earlier education was at Newcastle, where the family lived for some years.

money was of small importance, but he was always careful enough of his pence to make sure he got the best value for the least outlay.

It has been questioned at times how Mrs. Gorton's came to be selected. It was probably (though it cannot be verified with other than partial accuracy) that Smith learned of the school from a country medical practitioner who was sometimes a guest at Rowaleyn, Smith's country house. This was Dr. James Buchanan, of Dumbarton.

Buchanan's daughter was already at Mrs. Gorton's, entered there at a cousin's recommendation, when Madeleine was enrolled. It meant a friendly companion was available to look after the girl in her new surroundings, and an approved local contact would thus be able to keep an eye on her—the Victorians were particular about the protection and chaperonage of children when away from home.

* * *

When she arrived at 11 Clapton Terrace, Upper Clapton Road, Madeleine was disappointed only because it was an ordinary establishment, perhaps less ornate than imagination had pictured it.

Clapton, in Hackney Parish, was then sparsely settled. The Terrace was in the "elegant" part, a place of houses mostly in their own grounds. On every side were green or tilled fields with the rural Lea to capture the eye, and there was Mrs. Alice Gorton.

She was a small, anxious woman possessed of a warmth of heart and a nature so kind the very thought of distress in others depressed her. Mr. Gorton, in that not unusual fashion of some Victorian husbands, seems either non-existent or a wraith never noted down by men. Of his wife there is a letter from one of her pupils recalling her so pleasantly she closely resembles little "Miss Matty" in *Cranford*.

The handful of girls she looked after were well cared-for, and gently treated, this in an age when most forms of schooling, even for girls, were spartan.

Madeleine found it strange at first. Though her diction was good and almost free from the mild Doric prevailing on her family hearth, she still possessed enough of it to amuse her Sassenach companions. Mrs. Gorton is the authority in saying that during her first week the new girl was advised "midden is not a word for a young lady's tongue" and she was to refrain from using outlandish expressions like "fash." For her comfort there was the acquaintance from home, Mary Jane Buchanan, the doctor's daughter from Dumbarton, who grew to be a close friend.

Daily routine was simple in the large shabby house. One homely remembrance is of a wooden "Black Boy in a chipp'd turban" which stood in the hall holding a tray bearing a pot containing a trailing plant.

The girls—there were seventeen of them—slept in twos and threes in separate rooms. Madeleine was at the top, with Mary Buchanan, in a room with windows looking across the fields to Stamford. Perhaps it was there they first exchanged vows that whichever one married first, the other would be her bridesmaid.

Early rising was compulsory when the girls in gay, harsh* colours attended first prayers. After breakfast came piano lessons and practice, discussions on current affairs, tatting, netting, and general needlework, with, above all, deportment. There were also "ladylike pursuits" intended to fit the pupils into the adult world.

Mrs. Gorton liked to see her girls reading devotional works and attending both mid-week and all Sunday church services. On the Sabbath the whole school, and some of the domestics, went to St. James's Chapel, Lower Clapton, where the Rev. James Powell was noted for his able, discreet sermons.

His curate, the Rev. Nathaniel Woodard, came at regular intervals to Clapton Terrace to impart a more elaborate religious instruction. He is noted down as "a dark, well-set

---

* Perkins' aniline dye discoveries had yet to come and supplant the prevailing crude shades in general use.

young man of pleasing looks." It would seem Mrs. Gorton was not above exposing her charges to occasional masculine company in the safe protection of clerical garb.

There were regular walks, for exercise was something of a fetish, in all weathers. It was a morning event, at 11 o'clock, to see the girls moving along Upper Clapton Road to the turnpike, and left to Lea Bridge Road. From there they would walk between the wide expanses of North and South Mills Fields to the "neat iron bridge over the Lea on the Layton road."

In the fields, beyond Essex Wharf, was deep country with several paths. Once there, several minutes' undirected strolling in pairs was permitted.

During Madeleine's first year was the Great Exhibition at Hyde Park, which was both an event and an adventure. Going there involved a "long journey in Mr. George Kendall's omnibus." Mrs. Gorton escorted the party in person. No doubt she was in a state of excitement, knowing she and one pupil-teacher had to watch over seventeen lively girls for a full day.

There were local visits to the grounds of Spring House, and the notable event of May Day when the pretty daughter of Brune (a farmer near World's End) was queen, with attendant absurdities by Jack o' the Green and his "absurd troupe."

It was perhaps the trivia of a carefully regulated existence, precisely noted down by a girl whose frugal treats were enjoyed with her companions at a time when simple things remained in the memory.

In the detailed letters she wrote every Wednesday and Saturday to her parents, Madeleine explained her round and her happiness in it, doing so at length—even at that age she was a prolific correspondent; Edmund Pearson somewhat rashly calls her "one of the great letter writers of all time." In one incomplete recital of gossip she mentioned with alarm the Paris *coup d'état* which happened while she was at Mrs. Gorton's and which was the natural consequence of the 1848

Revolution in which Emile Langelier, reputedly, took a somewhat dramatic part.

                    *   *   *

The period of schooling was largely uneventful. No con-
secutive history remains of daily life at the time, other than
this record. Apart from the Great Exhibition, one other
important outing was mentioned. This was to swell the
mourning crowds at the Duke of Wellington's funeral, an
event which was as much the funeral of an era as today would
regard the death of Churchill.

Madeleine's behaviour was apparently good. She was
"diligent, attentive, and exceeding bright." This sounds like
Mrs. Gorton, the school-mistress, the conventional terms of
the usual report. The Miss Matty in that patient lady shone out
when she decided Madeleine could "be most provoking" and
given to "stubborn 'sulks' which at times quite alarmed us."

The girl possessed, or did not reveal, little of her later
individuality. Perhaps she was being careful, yet there is an
odd omen in knowing that "dear Mr. Woodard thought her
very striking with the makings of quite a little 'bewty' some
day."

It is an unexpected reaction from a curate and arouses a
feeling that perhaps Mr. Woodard felt her sexual attraction,
which moved his simple heart to such bold recognition.

In the later days of the Edinburgh trial, a Mrs. Walcot
(previously Augusta Guibilei, one of the two pupil-teachers
at Clapton Terrace who gave instruction in return for being
taught), was to declare: "I recollect one evening, in the
course of reading, it was mentioned that Swiss mountaineers
took arsenic to improve their breathing for ascending hills."
Mary Jane Buchanan was to refer, less specifically, to the
same matter at the same time.

It is not unlikely such a conversation did occur, and it is
also likely it arose from the reading of an article in *Chamber's
Journal.**

* "The Poison-Eaters", *Chamber's Journal*, December 1851, see p. 391,
Trial of Madeleine Smith (Notable British Trials, 1927).

At Mrs. Gorton's Madeleine received from home each number of the *Journal*, as well as the *Ladie's Own Journal*, and the *Scottish Guardian*. Mrs. Gorton was liberal-minded enough to allow her girls to choose much of their reading matter; the article could easily have been observed and discussed by the news-hungry maidens.

When at last the pleasures of Mrs. Gorton's and rural Clapton drew to an end, Madeleine Smith was to depart just as any other pupil had departed.

She had made no stir or scandal, behaving with the same undistinguished decorum as her companions. The few times she has been mentioned in letters can only be because she was from distant Scotland—the two other girls also from afar, Mary Jane Buchanan and a young woman from Canada, received equal attention in those same letters. Nothing in Madeleine's future portended in her behaviour; the reaction of Mr. Woodard was the sole direct comment together with those of Mrs. Gorton.

It can be pondered if the clergyman's view was sparked by the girl's attractions, to be hastily qualified and excused with discreet phrasing. She never did become a "bewty," not that she needed any such superficial gilt.

*   *   *

She left Mrs. Alice Gorton at the end of the 1853 summer term; she had been back to Scotland only once during her London visit. Apparently, when she left for good, it was to join her parents "at Glenapp under Girvan." This reference is isolated and infers either the Smiths were staying there with friends, or had perhaps rented a place for the season.

There is no informative word of Madeleine's return, not even a hint from pertinacious historians who probed so deeply four years later: did she ever have further contact with 11 Clapton Terrace? It seemed to stay unchanged for a time (her sister, Bessie, was to attend there), yet it remains a mystery. Just after Madeleine's departure Mrs. Gorton either gave up the school—perhaps she died—or went away.

In any case she disappeared from the local scene as a person. It is irresistible to ask what became of this kindly woman whose only epitaph is in a few yellowing letters by her and about her, treasured by the descendants of those who originally owned them. It seems a pity she never wrote, although so well qualified to do so, a full account of the one pupil in her school whose formative years are of such interest.

Words or sentences found in other private writings show Madeleine to have lost all trace of the Doric, and to have become a well-informed young woman with a mind of her own, and to whom some of Mrs. Gorton's liberal views seem to have clung.

There had been big houses along Upper Clapton Road. The girls of so excellent a school—allowed, in a moderate way, more licence than most—would have been given hospitality by well-to-do local gentlefolk. The freedom they enjoyed of Spring House emphasises the matter of being frequently received on proper occasions, and London, being so near, would have added knowledge which sent Madeleine back to Scotland a more mature, much less provincial girl than when she had left it.

There are two remaining glimpses of adolescent days, before she stepped on the threshold of history. She attended a ball some time in 1854 when she was at a country house near Govan Village. She wore "white silk stockings," a "fetching Tarlatan dress" and her hair was "arranged in falling ringlets," a charming picture.

Somewhere about the same time her heart was engaged by a young man in Edinburgh, whom she knew well. He exists only as "that amusing Charles"; it appears to have been a casual, teen-age devotion which left no real mark on her, nor regrets of a serious nature when he died less than two years later.

It is unfortunate that printed gossip was mainly confined to the wealthy or the notorious. Modern methods of attention to the smallest, dullest activities of the common man would have seen to it that Madeleine's youth was well reported

instead of remaining largely an unsolvable mystery at a time
when her adult character was being formed.

And formed it was, close to, but at the time without knowledge of, the tawdry world of Emile Langelier.

CHAPTER THREE

The Flame is Kindled

*Between L'Angelier and Madeleine Smith a social chasm
gaped which ordinarily would have proved impossible to
bridge.*

Edgar Lustgarten: *The Woman in the Case.*

THE HOPES OF Jersey were blasted in the cold realities of
Scotland. Of the dream remained only the problem of day-
to-day existence.

When Sir Francis Mackenzie died, Emile was distraught
and overcome. The mercurial temperament fell into the
depths so easy for his Gallic soul.

He feared at once about his employed days with Dicksons,
his position gained with the influence of his dead patron; it
would clearly come to an immediate end. This meant he
would not even have enough money to remain at his cheap
lodging hard by Tolbooth Church.

But at Dicksons' Waterloo Place shop he had shown his
devotion to detail and a charming natural courtesy.

William Richardson, the senior partner, professed himself
satisfied with his Jersey employee and said so in an interview
Emile had anticipated with dread; a pathetic note to his
mother mentions this, as does its jubilant successor. His work
was approved; he was to stay on.

But the dull days were to place their dimming touch on
his outlook. He was never to like Edinburgh (it can be
wondered if he ever passed the justice buildings in Parliament
House Square with any premonitory twinge). Scotland was
chill and grey, and he had more than a normal share of
colds. He aroused maternal alarm over this by wondering if
he had a "consumption of the lungs." As his next letter is

20

of a fine evening with two companions in Leith, it can be assumed he had briefly toyed with a notion, which, nevertheless, made Melanie uneasy.

The chronology of his life in places is confused. He paid a visit to St. Helier in 1846. It became either a surprisingly long leave or he had left Dicksons. His mother must have paid his fare; on his small salary such journeys were beyond him. Edinburgh repelled him, but in ignoring him it will be seen he was to react with what was a resentment, and a determination to make the city aware of him—this he managed to do, in an entirely different way.

* * *

It was a changed Emile who returned. The old charm and filial obedience remained, but he had filled out, matured, and was whiskered in an elegant fashion.

He talked of strange worlds, of things beyond Melanie's comprehension. She observed in him a bold front, an eye for a pretty girl, and a love of dress she considered out of place.

No longer had he time for the simplicities of the family circle, and, dutiful churchgoer as he always was, she learned-with real dismay he was not particular about his religion—the True Faith of his fathers no longer concerned him. Church was church, and that was all. In him were either the seeds of a casual heresy, or an advanced outlook concerned only with devotions uninfluenced by creed.

Achille was a big young man now, at his majority, and implementing Melanie's meagre income. Little Zephirine was a growing beauty of fifteen with a quaint, old-fashioned manner, still not strong and passionately loved by her mother for being the weakest of the brood. Elmire was a giggling schoolgirl of twelve.

Anastasie, in the full blush of womanhood, was being courted by a young farmer from 'the lonely village of Rosel.' Each Saturday he made the cart journey to St. Helier and though he was only recalled as "Tomkin,"* he was well liked.

---

* A curious name, not in the least Gallic, which has no other qualification. Anastasie did not marry him.

He appears to have sat on the family council (grandfather Claude de la Croix was dead) when Emile's future was discussed.

A suggestion arose which ended in arrangements being made for Emile to visit Paris where a thriving group of de la Croix was to be found and would welcome him. No doubt Saunders, always a staunch Langelier adherent, was asked for his views.

Whether or not Dicksons was consulted is not clear. Melanie's sense of duty would have seen to such a thing being done as a matter of course. It can only be surmised, yet Elmire, years later, recalled a continuous maternal uneasiness about the eldest son. In some way, possibly through his father's death and the Mackenzie tragedy, Emile always had something unspoken at the back of his mind.

The new front made this superficial Emile a stranger in some ways, standing apart from a family devotion and an allegiance always so embracing. Youthful idealism may have been warped in a nature inexperienced in coping with unusual stresses and a natural vanity in no way improved by feminine admiration—he always got a lot of it. Life in Scotland, and his own efforts to hide his uncertainty, had made him outwardly a different man.

Paris was the worst place for him. A job was easily obtained, in a merchant's office as a clerk, but the careless city was too much so for his sense of responsibility.

He took at once to the life of the Boulevards, to the cheap, lower class café-society of fellow clerks and new friends, discovering that plentiful wine cost mere pennies, and both women and morals were casual.

French custom saw to it that Langlier became the more impressive (originally correct) L'Angelier. This Emile adopted and refused to have changed. Except in Jersey, where the change was unacceptable, it was his permanent name.

He got into no serious trouble, acquiring the true Parisian braggadocio as became a man of the world—perfumed, dandified, and well aware of his good looks. He grew adept at parlour-tricks, facile poetry, and the glibness of current cant. His nature was overlaid with florid graces a Gascon could not have bettered.

In general the Paris stay was orthodox and conventional. He was there at the time of the Revolution of 1848—of which Madeleine wrote concerning the later *coup d'état* which grew from its roots—when Louis Philippe fled from the political heat of Paris to the sobriety of England.

One thing worth noting is that Emile's future grand talk of his part in this was, in fact, most trivial. He was for two weeks an untrained recruit in civil volunteer forces maintaining law and order. His sole task of any importance was in a group of young men in arm-bands set to guard a suburban railway goods-siding.

Out of this came at least one gain in the friendship he made with one young man in that company of guards. This was Charles De Rosen, son of a Belgian aristocrat. The pair went about together, and it resulted in Emile's only break from Paris. For a month, in the summer of 1850, he was guest of the Baron De Rosen and his wife at their home a few miles from Malmédy, where Emile spent a period in splendid surroundings which did not fail to raise his eyes to the advantages of wealth and position.

Whatever his hopes for the future, he was back in Jersey in 1851.

Little Zephirine was dead.

*   *   *

Madame Langelier took it badly. She adored the girl and the blow was heart-rending. The family closed ranks; Emile —who was deeply fond of his sister—temporarily abandoned his showy mannerisms.

Once again the sable-clothed mourners, and the crape-hung funeral procession, headed for Green Street Cemetery where the dead girl was buried with her father.

Melanie became prostrate. The last decade had seen the death of her husband and the failure of her hopes in Emile, and her hopes for him. She had believed the new decade would have been kinder to her, and now the favourite had gone. It was as well for her peace of mind that she did not know within the same decade she would lose both her sons.

Emile was restless almost at once. The provincialism of the island was depressing and on the pretext of furthering his life—perhaps he was driven by an impetus he could not understand—he desired a return to Scotland. His character indicates he may have resented Edinburgh's indifference and with his newly acquired Parisian polish, felt it would be sure to fall at his feet; Elmire was to judge it this way.

With what money there was and what he had saved, he decided to leave. Melanie was bewildered by this, but again Elmire is the authority for believing the mother was neither happy nor at ease in her son's company, this stranger with glittering cosmopolite manners and false airs. It is specious to wonder what his fate would have been, had Sir Francis Mackenzie lived. Emile might have settled down to a good, sober marriage and decent old age without ever descending into the hell Glasgow was to be for him. There is this—he was the perfect example of the man requiring discipline and control under which his best features would have been encouraged. Rudderless, he yielded from sheer lack of character, to the worst in himself.

He was not, as Edgar Lustgarten claims, "always a mean and cunning opportunist with an undeviating eye on personal advantage." This is facile judgment. Woolly-minded, at the mercy of his instincts, and by turns prig, amateur Don Juan, and snobbish liar, Emile was also the classic example of excellent material spoiled by circumstances and the lack of a guiding hand on a nature desperately needing it. The preacher seeking a moral in the story of sound wood spoiled by the indifferent workman would have found it in Emile L'Angelier.

*   *   *

Dicksons had no place for him. There was a small job in a shop which lasted for a few weeks. He had taken up quarters

in the Rainbow Tavern, North Bridge, where he shared a
bed, on the score of cheapness, with a servitor. This tavern
was kept by a man named Baker, who must have been
generous. He allowed Emile to remain when he had no
money at all.

Paris had increased his desires of becoming a lady-killer,
even when he was without funds. He was involved in several
minor affairs of the heart not quite so ornate, but a great
deal more authentic, than that designated at the later trial
as "the young lady in Fife." She certainly existed but never
counted to the extent Emile was to claim—it was a mixture
of small truth and much embroidered exhibitionism. His real
love at the time was a waitress in an eating-house, a decent
girl who refused to take him seriously; he did not fail to
dress her into a veritable *fata morgana*, and went into
dramatic frenzies when she would not marry him.

A friend of his, the Rainbow Tavern servitor, was to
declare at the trial a picture of the aftermath:

> I did not know much of his ways. I was not much out with
> him. He was very easily excited. He was at times subject to low
> spirits. I have often seen him crying at night. Latterly, before
> he went to Dundee, he told me he was tired of his existence
> and wished himself out of the world. He said so on more than
> one occasion. I remember on one occasion he got out of bed
> and went to the window and threw it up. I rose out of bed and
> went to him, and he said if I had not disturbed him he would
> have thrown himself out. The windows of the Rainbow are
> about six storeys from the ground—the height of the North
> Bridge, indeed. He was in the habit very often of getting up at
> night and walking up and down the room in an excited state,
> weeping very much. I happened to know he had at that time
> met with a disappointment in a love matter. He did not tell
> me so himself, but I heard my uncle speak of it. I heard
> L'Angelier speak to other people about it. It was some lady
> in Fife.

This friend, named Baker and nephew of the tavern-
keeper, had lived in St. Helier and should have known Emile

better—the adventitious lady of Fife was overlaid in that untidy mind with the closer, more genuine emotions about the waitress.

Emile was not the type to kill himself, nor could he seriously have visualised it. It is a fact he liked to contemplate the deed and alarm his friends in doing so; in this he was at his childish worst. He once confided to Anastasie: "I would never commit suicide unless I could be there to contemplate it"—the hall-mark of the true exhibitionist.

He was fortunate that his charm had a way of remaining in some men's memories. It did so with a Mr. William Pringle Laird, of Nethergate, Dundee.

Laird came across him in his misery at the Rainbow Tavern and generously recruited him as an extra hand at his nursery and seed shop,* offering a few shillings a week salary with bed and board. It was a living, and better than crawling home to Jersey.

Life in Dundee was for the moment more interesting than Edinburgh. In those days it was not a city and possessed none of Edinburgh's intellectual standards; the wave of industrial expansion had not fully started. Emile soon found it was no more than the peaceful royal burgh it had been for so many years.

His new job began in January, 1852, with one of his inevitable colds. This he threw off swiftly and proceeded to impress his new employer with his work, or at least his zest for it.

Being Emile, he could not resist mourning out loud for his most recent lost love—at times it became almost an occupational passion—but Laird did not take it too seriously, even if he had to endure much of it, for Emile lived in his employer's house at Blackness, behaving so well that Mrs. Downie, Laird's aunt-housekeeper, took such a liking to him she treated him as if he were her own son.

* It is curious that Emile, with no talent for it, went so often into the profession of his father. At least once the chronicler has read a magazine article which made a pseudo-Freudian hotch-potch of this, drawing a bogus moral from Œdipus with a sort of literary sleight of hand.

He made a friend (he avoided real intimacy) of a fellow employee named Pringle—they shared the same bedroom at Blackness. There was a second friend in William Ogilvie, a cashier at the Dundee Banking Company, who, as honorary secretary of the Floral and Horticultural Society, convened its monthly meetings in the commodious back part of Laird's Nethergate shop. To these men Emile played his favourite role of would-be suicide with morbid relish (Elmire later claimed "Emile often talked of suicide. He liked himself too much, even when he was sad, to do such a thing. More than that, he was much too frightened of pain").

Some of this talk he tried, with more success, on his closest friend in Dundee. This was an upholsterer of Nethergate named Andrew Smith. His home was across the Tay in Newport and, despite its moments of gloom, liked Emile's company so much that occasional week-ends at Newport became something of an institution. Of Emile's excitable disposition Smith was to declare at the trial: "Self destruction was a very frequent subject of conversation with him. I thought him serious, though I never had any serious apprehension that he would do it. That was from want of courage."

*   *   *

Dundee was not big enough for Emile. He grew restless (and told Melanie so in a letter). For all the job and the comfort at Laird's, he wanted to be in new surroundings.

In July of that year he expressed a wish to try for a situation in Glasgow. Many people in Dundee liked him, and the most influential of them readily gave him excellent recommendations with which to try his luck. Among them was William Pringle Laird, who was generous enough and thought enough of him to say that if efforts failed in Glasgow, the Nethergate job and the Blackness bedroom would remain open for him, if he desired to return.

This hunger for betterment was purely material, and not, as one irresponsible magazine article has put it, the prompting of predestination; such metaphysical assumptions tend to

dramatise a simple action. Emile was bound for "golden
Glasgow"—as Sacheverell Sitwell regards it in a poetic
treatment of the case—because he was on the verge of thirty
and was anxious to improve his somewhat indifferent com-
mercial progress; sudden phases of bettering himself were an
old story to his family.

He found lodgings in the house of Mrs. Elizabeth Wallace,
in Kingston Place, Glasgow. This was on the south side of
the Clyde, in Tradeston, and not too much of a strain on his
slender purse.

While he was there, getting to know the town and inter-
viewing without success various likely employers, he spent
his evening hours mooning about or playing his guitar (his
eldest sister considered he had an "indifferent tenor voice").
He told his trusting landlady about his hard times and how
they affected an ex-lieutenant of the Navy. Why he, least
nautical of human beings, should have told such a story is a
mystery, for though Mrs. Wallace was to speak well of him,
she implied that even she could not swallow such a yarn.

By September, having failed hopelessly in his efforts, his
luck served him well. An elderly lady, on a visit to Glasgow,
met him in the street and recalled him as an acquaintance
she had made in Edinburgh when he had frequently sold her
flowers at Dicksons. That she remembered him so well is
typical; her liking was proved by her immediate efforts on
his behalf.

She procured for him the situation of packing clerk, at a
tiny salary, with Huggins and Company, merchants and ware-
housemen, of 10 Bothwell Street. It was her personal
approach to her husband's friend, William Huggins, and
Emile's excellent recommendations, which clinched the
arrangement. Her kind action done, she appears no more in
his story but whether or not she was an unintentional evil
genius is a matter for students of the abstract who enjoy
such matters.

It was a humble job carrying a wage of £26 a year, and a
small living allowance. He was able to start at once, and

liked the place. The firm appeared to like him, and his work. It was not long before his talent for making friends began to help him in this new town. It was as much natural gregariousness as dislike for his cheap and sordid lodgings. With friends there would be places to visit, homes where he would be welcome, and companionship better than his guitar.

Little happened to him in 1853, except for one letter from Melanie which arrived to say that Achille, on whom she had pinned such hopes in the absence of Emile, had taken a sudden chill. He could not be cured and was dead.

It brought her the deepest distress. Emile was equally afflicted. Achille Jean had never been his close companion, but between them was the strong bond of brothers who appreciated each other and each other's company.

What was unfortunate was the lack of money with which Emile could go home; he could scarcely ask so soon for leave from Huggins and Company. He was doing well and realised he dare not again risk his future advancement. The cost of the funeral, too, precluded any remittance from Jersey.

It was his new friends who heartened him, people like Tom Kennedy, Huggins' cashier, who often offered the hospitality of his Partickhill house to the bereft young man. Other places were also made available to him, such as in the company of August de Mean, Chancellor of the French Consulate, whose bachelor lodgings excelled with good company.

Emile's nearest second approach to the many grand (and fictitious) friends of whom he often talked was William D'Esterre Roberts, a successful merchant and a director of the Patriotic Assurance Company. Roberts was so sorry for his young chance acquaintance, he asked him to his home in Woodside Place on Christmas Day where, for once, Emile was to enjoy a mild festivity far removed from the dullness of his room (the Roberts' family, like many orthodox Scots church-goers at the time, scarcely if at all celebrated Christmas). It was such a happy day in its earlier parts that he drew a sharp rebuke from Anastasie, who thought his letter home about it was "untimely." He was, on that occasion, very unwell after the evening meal even if it was no more than one of the gastric upsets to which he had become subject.

Glasgow was a fine place for a penniless young man. There was much to be seen and to do (even if he was to write feelingly, "what a curious climate of wet and foggy weather Glasgow is").

He grew to understand something of the Scots, slow to friendship and cautious with mirth. They were kind to him once they had overcome their suspicions of his origins and florid manners—the French were not wholly acceptable at the time. With his gift for presenting his own case, he probably made it clear that small, proudly independent Jersey was certainly not French, or, for that matter, in any way English. It would have appealed to the insularity of his adopted countrymen and their natural prejudice for conquered lands determined to retain their personalities.

It had been just before Christmas that Emile, aware of the social values of a religious meeting ground, chose St. Jude's Episcopal Church in Jane Street for his attendance.

His choice may have been chance, or, which is not unlikely, because St. Jude's was the only Church of England establishment in the town. Perhaps it was also due to Melanie's interest in things English; if his way was to be set in Scotland, he could at least attend the right church—his one error in her eyes was that he continued to remain in the Protestant fold.

It emphasises his wisdom in sometimes doing the right thing; he did not go near any of the Roman Catholic churches on the sure basis that with his background he might be acceptable as a Protestant, but allegiance to his father's faith would have closed many doors now open to him. There was nothing in Emile which overlooked a reasonable method of progress; in this his practicality and common sense were purely French.

He made friends at the church, which was almost in

Blythswood Square, and one acquaintance in Mary Arthur Perry, to whom he was introduced by an English visitor, a Miss Mary Philpot.

Mary Perry was a spinster, not particularly old but old for an unmarried woman in those days. The younger daughter of a highly respected drysalter, she had become isolated in the joy of her single state—both her brother and sister were married. She lived in her father's large house at 144 West Renfrew Street, with an adequate allowance and complete freedom. Small, greying, discreet and bespectacled, she was eminently a woman fit to be on her own. She embellished her quiet existence by sharing the lives of others, and was, in her soft and kind-hearted way, to play a large part in Emile's last years.

The friendship grew and to Miss Perry can be attributed his awareness that Tradeston was definitely on the wrong side of the river. It did not go with St. Jude's nor with people like William Roberts, and Miss Perry's circle.

Firmly determined to better himself, Emile was to be found, at his own insistence, lodgings at the other end of Glasgow, far removed from the social level of Tradeston and neighbouring Gorbals, where already the blight of slums was bringing it into disfavour.

The incumbent of St. Jude's, the Reverend Charles Popham Miles, was both an affable man and a brilliant one. He was not only an M.A., but a qualified M.D., whose great passion in life was antiques. It is possible (it can be only partially verified) he took a particular interest in Emile, a baptised Roman Catholic and therefore something of a mild triumph as a convert. In those days of sharply defined religious schisms, such a conversion—shown in regular church attendance—can explain Miles' interest.

In any case he took it on himself to find the young man a better home, one in keeping with his financial position, and pleasing to Jane Street.

A lodging was found in the home of Peter Clark, Curator of the Royal Botanic Garden. Operated by the Royal Botanic

Institution, it was well out on Great Western Road, a place
of beauty with the River Kelvin bordering its north-western
side to lend pleasure for the contemplative eye of the wanderer along the wooded banks. The Curator's house was
indeed a change from Tradeston.

Mrs. Margaret Clark welcomed Emile as a paying guest
and was particularly kind to him. A homely woman who
listened to him with interested patience, she must have won
his admiration; he was there from May, 1854, to July, two
years later, almost a record for him.

*   *   *

It has been suggested that Emile first saw Madeleine Smith
in Sauchiehall Street, or on the way home from Sunday
church service.

It is known he was instantly attracted to her, but he
would have had little time for wandering about business
streets—in Glasgow work was hard and hours were long—
and Jane Street was not then a church to which Madeleine
had ever been. The Smiths attended the United Presbyterian
Church in Gordon Street to sit under the eye of the Rev.
A. O. Beattie, a very old family friend; their journeys
between church and home were made in their carriage.

There is a small, feasible clue in another direction. The
Botanic Garden was a popular place in the summer and
Madeleine went there once or twice that year with members
of her family. That being so, Emile, without spare money,
would have spent frequent time in his large "garden" where
he could have caught his first glimpse of her—Mrs. Clark
mentions him having spoken about "a lady. I don't exactly
remember when he did so; it was while he lived in my house.
I think it was in the first year that he lived with me."

The supposition seems strengthened. It would have been
easy for him to discover, from one of the uniformed atten-
dants, who she was, the unknown charmer. In that circumscribed place the daughter of a very well-known architect

would have been at once recognisable, unless Emile were
with one of his many acquaintances at the time who may
have supplied the desired information.

Perhaps there was the flutter of a hand or eye, perhaps a
meaning look. Emile was a striking figure, and would have
been impressive in the clothes he took such care of, and the
stove-pipe hat of the day. Being Emile and more French than
anything else, he would have gazed on her boldly, with open
admiration. In Scotland or England the furtive side-glance
was the first gesture of male interest, but learned on the
Continent, where women like frank admiration and expect
it, Emile's stare would have been without reticence.

He was certainly smitten on seeing her. To his highly
susceptible emotions this plain and ordinary girl doubtless
manifested that powerful sexual attraction which was her
call to men.

Whether he was dismayed or downcast on learning who
she was is a matter of conjecture. The distantly seen daughter
of a socially prominent man must have appeared far removed
from his circle—the levels in the 1850s were clearly marked
and difficult to climb. A penniless packer, of no background,
cannot have hoped to get across the wide gap of class.

Yet Emile, with knowledge of his own magnetism for
women, cannot have been dismayed. He was well installed
within the hospitable kindness of the St. Jude's ladies. It
might be assumed, with some reason, that Madeleine had
kindled his imagination, caused him to raise the sights on
his future in getting into view an alliance suitable both for
his heart and happiness. He was the son of a republican-
minded man who had held, and had taught his children, that
worth alone mattered, that money was incidental and class
a thing of accent, not value.

Emile determined he would meet her. With his ability to
apply himself to the object in view, he set about finding
methods of obtaining that one essential to gain a footing
with people of a higher sphere, a proper introduction.

He was, it has often been said, after Madeleine's money

and position. The Smiths had five children and some wealth, so, it can be asked, what money?

As to her position, it was no more than a matter of friends and their acceptance of her.

CHAPTER FOUR

Passionate Delirium

*Papa was very angry with me for walking with a gentleman
unknown to him. I told him we had been introduced and I
saw no harm in it.*

Madeleine Smith.

THE SMITHS WERE indeed a family of some local importance,
and of great probity and respectability.

James Smith was an architect of distinction with offices at
123, later 124, St. Vincent Street. He had many responsibilities
from a director's chair in the North British Insurance Company through a range of other lucrative matters to a purely
ornamental position on the Council of Glasgow Fine Art
Association. His beginnings had been humble, however. At
the time of Madeleine's birth he, a crofter's son, had been
little more than a builder, but his rise to affluence was swift.

He rented part of a house at 16 India Street, where he
kept servants and his own carriage. There was, too, the
country house, Rowaleyn, designed by himself with inspiration clearly provided by Glamis Castle or it may have been
some Rhenish stronghold he had seen. This was at Row,
on the Gareloch* about twenty-four miles along the Clyde
from Glasgow.

Strong-minded and certain of himself, but now without
his full beard, James was the stern, somewhat sharp-tempered
Victorian patriarch in person. He did not suffer fools gladly,
expected an impeccably run home and would have been both
baffled and at sea were he confronted by a type like Emile
L'Angelier.

* Not the Gairloch on the north-east coast, an estate of Sir Francis
Mackenzie, Emile's dead patron.

35

He had married the daughter of a famous architect in 1832, but it is puzzling where he could have found the unusual name of Madeleine for his eldest child—his wife's name, Elizabeth, was bestowed on her second daughter, Bessie.

Mrs. Smith, neither good in health nor in constitution, was given to megrims (the migraine of today). She had taken early to the uniform of matrimony, retreating into a world of babies and domesticity broken by such outings as she could endure.

In all she had five children, just as the Langeliers in Jersey and in almost the same order. Apart from the two older girls there was John, known as Jack, then about fifteen; Janet, who was eleven, and little James, just on nine years old.

Bessie went to Mrs. Gorton's (or to whoever had taken over the school), and had just completed her education when Madeleine met Emile for the first time.

Madeleine's was the typical sheltered life of the girl of her class. There were At Homes, routs, balls, and enjoyments of every sort in which she was expected to share. The family social life was extremely busy at all times.

Her days were peaceful and well ordered, where servants rose early and worked hard, where houses were cold and fires large in over-furnished rooms depressing with heavily patterned wall-paper, where morning prayers were as much a part of existence as the precisely arranged protocol within and without the home.

In that substantial India Street house, Madeleine's pleasures and pursuits were conventional. As variations she had frequent trips to Edinburgh, a matter of forty miles away, to Rowaleyn for the summer (which old-fashioned people continued to spell as Roualeyn), or to her grandfather's model farm near Ardrossan.

She enjoyed reading both the novels which were now becoming acceptable in polite society, and the heavier material such as the new and brightly illustrated edition of Gibbon's *Decline and Fall of the Roman Empire* just issued

by the useful Mr. Bohn (an account remains from venerable
Mr. Ogilvie, of St. Vincent Street, dated 1854 for "1 Bohn,
ill. ed.—taken by Miss Smith").

Her routine seldom varied. She breakfasted in bed at
seven ("but I dont rise till 9 o'c"); her mornings were largely
devoted to reading, writing, or music, the afternoons to
formal calls or shopping. Her mother required her regular
assistance in the house, but in mere token duties too trivial
for the three servants.

Small, rather timorous, and blonde fading to brown, Mrs.
Smith expected Madeleine to learn from her; it may be her
doubtful health at times required an efficient substitute. This
good lady had become completely effaced by her husband's
strength of character. She was obedient and passive, the
product of an earlier age (though she was only forty-one at
the time, seven years her husband's junior) to whom clung
the thoughts and manners of the Georges and their ritualistic
civilisation. She was humourless and easily perturbed—the
later emancipation of women (which Madeleine was to
approve) would have prostrated her. It was difficult to discuss
with her matters outside the family circle: "Mother is very
good," Madeleine wrote, "but you cannot make a confidante
of her. I could not open my heart to her."

She effaced herself during Madeleine's subsequent life,
and though furtive glimpses will be seen of the family, Mrs.
Smith, except for a couple of appearances, faded into an
obscurity as complete as that covering Mrs. Gorton; it
epitomises her that her husband once spoke, in a moment
of unusual sentiment, of her as "a *dear* little woman"; the
remark was long treasured by the family which heard it and
it became, years after, a gibe guaranteed to provoke the
laughter marking all such inter-family humour.

With her own family Madeleine was bright, clear-minded
and frequently opinionated. She had her father's spirit and
did not hesitate to stand up to him (to a friend she wrote,
"Papa was hotly vexed when I defended the Empress
[Eugenie, wife of Napoleon III] and told him she was of

Scottish blood—he would not give in and I would not. How
we argued").

It was a happy, united little family, content with itself and
its circle . . . until Emile L'Angelier came on the scene.

*   *   *

Once having observed Madeleine he made consistent efforts
to meet her, failing to discover a method. He appears to
have seen her once or twice again and it can be taken that
he was enraptured; he thought of little else (in a letter home
about his feelings, he used the phrase "*quand l'amour*" as
part of a flowery elaboration; it seems rather pompous, as if
he had been reading a book; he was never particularly original
in thought).

The weeks must have run or dragged by, depending on his
variable temperament. The winter was severe and the Botanic
Garden would have been bleak and miserable. Each inclement
morning he had to endure the stuffy discomfort of Mr.
"Jamie" Walker's early omnibus which dropped him near
Bothwell Street, journeys he could ill afford—in all but
wholly bad weather he would walk the distance of barely
two miles. At that hour of the morning (the warehouse was
ready for business at eight), not even Emile can have hoped
to see a sign of his dream woman, yet must have scanned
each private window he passed; he did not then know of
India Street, not that it was on his route.

He tried every method he could devise to achieve his
object, casting about in the end to see what could be done
by devious means.

At last he learned (from warehouse gossip?) that a
fellow-worker named Mackenzie might be the key to the
problem.

Mackenzie was a middle-aged man who had, Emile found
out, a nephew named Baird, and the Bairds knew the Smiths.
He put his plans into operation by contriving to be asked to
the Bairds' house in Royal Crescent, where Charles and
Robert Baird lived with their widowed mother.

A friendship sprang up between Emile and Charles, but he was shrewd enough not to make a convenience of the upright Charles, who would have had no part of such a hungrily sought introduction; only recently his father, head of Baird and Muirhead, had died and Charles was overwhelmed with his new responsibilities.

Young Robert was much easier clay, a boy of seventeen and amenable to a charming worldling like Emile. Even here Glasgow class distinctions intruded. Robert Baird was induced to ask his uncle Mackenzie to arrange the introduction; it was flatly refused.

Then, again Emile's idea, young Baird approached his mother with the suggestion that Madeleine should be asked to one of her "evenings" when their new friend, L'Angelier, could also attend.

Maternal sharpness must have seen through such ingenuity. She would not countenance the scheme, even for her beloved Robert.

Though he pestered the boy on a number of occasions, Emile suddenly achieved his desire in a fortuitous combination of place and circumstance.

He was in Robert's company in Sauchiehall Street when, with the keen eye of the yearning lover, he spied Madeleine entering the draper's shop kept by Mr. Paterson—one day a letter from her was to say: "Did you or I fancy that first morning we met in Sauchiehall Street that we should yet be husband and wife."

How he must have urged Robert Baird on, to bring her out even with her female companion—it was Bessie, back from Mrs. Gorton's—to the doorstep where he would await them. His ebullient spirit doubtless soared into the grey sky, heavy with snow though it was, until the Glasgow scene, the busy streets, were momentarily lost to view in his dreams ... until she stood before him, on Mr. Paterson's prosaic step.

It is recorded she wore a sprigged gown, a brown *visite* (short, sleeveless cloak), and a "bonnet." What that could have been is unknown but, for the occasion, she would have been no true woman had she not ardently longed to have been wearing the finest bonnet in town.

It is fascinating to wonder about this meeting, so big an event in their lives. Her eye kindled when Robert made the formal introduction, for by her readiness to be introduced to the anxious young stranger, it is obvious the impression he had made on her.

He would have swept low his hat and bowed from the waist ("Emile," Elmire recalled, "was full of airs and graces"), and perhaps kissed her hand, which would have been most natural for him; such gestures never fail to enchant teen-age girls. There were, in fact, to be two criticisms from those who learned of the meeting: it was shocking in those days for a gentleman to be introduced to a lady on the open street, a grave breach of etiquette, and hand-kissing was supposed to be confined to saluting married women.

The ordinary passers-by could have noticed little, an elegant young lady of good class on a draper's doorstep, flanked by a guardian youth of her own cut. Before her, on the sidewalk, a foreign-looking young man defying, as those of foreign blood often do, exact social classification. Only those in the know would have recognised the daughter of a notable architect and the younger son of a recently dead, well-thought-of Writer to the Signet, and seen them engaged in conversation with one of Huggins' packing clerks.

What fires were lighted, what blood called to blood can only be based on the eternal verities of a man with a girl. They would have chatted, fumbled with the small change of gossip, and brought in friends all parties would surely know —the name of William D'Esterre Roberts (and obviously that of Baron De Rosen) would have been uttered by Emile both as personal recommendation and a proof that his airy explanations could include real persons.

Bessie would not have remained long with Mr. Paterson. She had to know all about it, who it was Bobbie Baird had brought for her sister to meet. Feminine curiosity did the rest and she, as well, formally met Emile, though he never "saw" her—he fails to mention if she also wore a sprigged gown, a *visite* and a bonnet.

But how his brown eyes must have talked the world's most ancient Esperanto; how he would have declared his emotions in those brief minutes. She answered him circumspectly, but more forthrightly than her times allowed, in the same secret fashion. She was Madeleine Smith and nobody has put her case better than Miss Tennyson Jesse:

> Hers was a nature which had to have adventure. In the World War she would have been an admirable member of society. She would have driven an ambulance, had sentimental little affairs with the wounded officers, been thoroughly competent and completely occupied. Had she been a medieval Italian she might have been a successful intriguer and removed people who inconvenienced her from her path, and seduced those whom she wished to seduce without any loss of social standing. As it was, she was born in that period of the world's history which was the most hopeless for a nature such as hers. Strength, determination, passion, ruthlessness were a bad foundation to be overlaid with the Victorian sentimentality which was also hers in full measure, and which, living when she did, she could hardly have avoided. It was her only outlet, and she sentimentalised to the full.*

Until recently it has been the fashion to ponder romantically the first meetings of lovers whose stories have moved or startled the world. It is possibly because most great lovers have been outcasts in their own generations and historians cannot help pretending that larks sang and portents were seen. Human nature demands a fanfare, a comet in the sky, when an eternal story is born.

But Nature, to whom meetings between men and women can have only a practical end in view, is not so ready to supply a suitable orchestra for the first step in an uncomplicated biological process.

Madeleine and Emile met for a few moments in the drear February of an overcast "golden Glasgow." No trumpets sounded, but within them perhaps they did; a romance had

* *Trial of Madeleine Smith* (Notable British Trials, 1927).

begun because of an introduction's formal spark. After all, Abelard would have been awkwardly placed if Uncle Fulbert had not made him tutor to Héloïse, and even Romeo had to get into Capulet's fair graces before he could reach Juliet.

*   *   *

After the introduction came brief, careful meetings. Every precaution had to be taken, it being difficult for Madeleine to escape unaccompanied from the house. Mrs. Smith liked to know what was going on and with three girls on her hands, made it her business to see they did not get into any mischief.

Once or twice the pair met at the bookseller's shop run by Mr. Ogilvie. It was close to James Smith's office in St. Vincent Street, on the same side, and when she visited her father, Madeleine could contrive to make the short errand on her own; browsing in a bookseller's demands its own peculiar form of isolation to which there are seldom any obstacles.

Emile had only to make an excuse to escape for a few minutes from the warehouse. Ogilvie's was not more than a quick dash away from Bothwell Street. In his working clothes and hatless, Emile's haste would have gone unremarked.

What confidences were exchanged or vows made can never be known, but within the shelter of the friendly bookseller's they had several meetings. If Mr. Ogilvie observed anything, he never revealed it. Booksellers are not unaware that lovers sometimes use them as screens against the world and these most charitable of men seldom object.

On two occasions they were able to arrange meetings when Madeleine paid visits to the local centre of a highly comprehensive music tuition. This was in Hill Street where the brothers Richard and Robert Adams, and their sister Edith, between them taught the piano, cornet, flute, violin, and concertina. Madeleine went there in the Smith brougham at least once on her own; she was able to spend thirty minutes with Emile. Another time she went with Bessie (their father, it can be assumed, approved the industry of the lively Adams' clan).

The authority for this is Emile, who wrote of it to Anastasie confessing, rather wryly, he had to pretend an interest in the cornet to get inside the house (this from an avowed guitarist). He gave a flower to Madeleine, and, somewhat mysteriously, a letter for her sent by way of Bessie; perhaps he was too shy to hand it over in person.

The first of the published letters which so distinguished the case came from Madeleine. It is undated, but may be attributed to March, 1855, when she was nineteen:*

My dear Emile—I do not feel as if I were writing to you for the first time. Though our intercourse has been very short yet we have become as familiar friends. May we long continue so. And ere lang may you be a friend of Papas is my most earnest desire—We feel it rather dull here after the excitement of a Towns life—But then we have much more time to devote to study and improvement. I often wish you were near us we could take such charming walks. One enjoys walking with a pleasant companion and where could we find one to equal yourself?

I am trying to break myself off all my *very* bad habits it is you I have to thank for this—which I do sincerely from my heart—Your flower is fading

"I never cast a flower away"
"The gift of one who cared for me"
"A little flower a faded flower"
"But it was done reluctantly"

I wish I understood botany for your sake as I might send you some specimens of moss. But alas I know nothing of that study. We shall be in Town next week. We are going to the Ball on the 20th of this month so we will be several times in Glasgow before that—Papa and Mama are not going to town next Sunday. So of course you must *not* come to Row. We shall not expect you—Bessie desires me to remember her to you. Write on Wednesday or Thursday. I must now say adieu. With kind love believe me your very sincerely
MADELEINE.

She was staying at Rowaleyn at the time though such stays were punctuated by frequent returns to Glasgow.

* She was born on March 29, 1835, at West Regent Street, Glasgow.

Her letter reveals warm feelings of friendship for Emile, but there is a hint of the censorious Jersiais about it. She was trying to break herself of "all my *very* bad habits." What these can have been is a mystery. Elmire was subsequently to admit Emile had his own ideas of how women should behave, and, so soon, he had begun Madeleine's reform. Her professed compliance reveals her feelings for him. There was a warning he must not turn up at Row, indicating that at an earlier meeting he must have hinted about coming to see her. It was a natural proposal, if indiscreet just then.

The next letter, posted on April 3, thanks Emile for his letter and mentions that "some friend" had seen them together: "Papa was very angry with me for walking with a Gentleman unknown to him." Bessie sided with her irritated father, and it can be wondered if Bessie was that "friend."

It might have been sisterly jealousy—both girls were certainly flirts—or the outcome of some quarrel between them. Bessie "does not know I am writing to you so dont mention it" (Madeleine was always original in punctuation and spelling, or in too much of a hurry to bother about it).

Her "heart tells me I am doing nothing wrong" so she clearly intends to go her own way, and gives suggestions for future chance meetings; "say you are astonished to see us in Town without letting you know." The first strands of a future web of deceit were being woven. Madeleine was never above lying when it was necessary, and could do it in an able and reassuring fashion.

Her days at Row were engaged in the usual household round, or in walks through the richly wooded country. The village itself (called Rhu today) was no more than a handful of scattered houses. There was much to see in the surrounding country; the shore of Loch Lomond was no more than a six-mile walk away, a favourite jaunt of hers.

She had to entertain people who were constantly visiting Rowaleyn or staying there. In a letter she complained, perhaps insincerely, of "friends friends staying with us which is a great annoyance to me." Her family were usually there in

force, with the consoling company of her brother, Jack, to
whom she was closer than to any of the others.

In Glasgow Emile was more frequently in the company of
little Miss Perry. To her he revealed a growing fondness for
Madeleine. "About the spring of 1855," Miss Perry was to
say in court, "I came to know him intimately; the intimacy
went on gradually. At the time he heard of his brother's
death (*sic*). He was in very great distress."

* * *

A fortnight later Madeleine wrote to Emile at the Botanic
Garden. She was alarmed and upset. Whether there had been
family intervention or she was perturbed at the warmth of
her feelings is to be guessed at; she wrote:

> My Dear Emile I now perform the promise I made in parting
> to write you soon—We are to be in Glasgow tomorrow
> (Thursday) but as my time shall not be at my own disposal
> I cannot fix any time to see you. Chance may throw you in
> my way. I think you will agree with me in what I intend pro-
> posing viz. That for the present the correspondence had better
> *stop*—I know your good feeling will not take this unkind it is
> meant quite the reverse. By continuing to correspond harm may
> arise In *dis*continuing it nothing can be said.

Her motives are puzzling, but most likely James Smith had
put his foot down. Her sop to her own conscience in her
earlier letter concerning the dictates of her heart can have
been an attempt at self-extenuation when she saw Papa
working up his ready choler. "The love I have for my
family," she wrote that year, "is a natural love—I love them
for they have been kind to me. But I must confess I fear
them—I could not confide in Father Brother Mother Sister.
I fancy they are the most indulgent parents—yet there is an
awe which should not be." It is, incidentally, not easy for the
modern world wholly to comprehend the impressive stature
of the mid-Victorian father. He was almost god-like, the
indisputable lord of the hearth, whose word was law and
whose least command was inviolate. To his family he was

not only made in the Divine image, but was nearly as fearsome and quite as dictatorial as his Maker.

Though Madeleine said the letters had "better *stop*", she was perfectly ready to receive one from Emile, if she did not meet him by chance in Glasgow for which she offered a plain hint as to her whereabouts in order to make such a "chance" meeting possible.

She was facing her first test and dealing with an attachment much more unacceptable to her family than it was to her.

The tradition of young love blighted by unfeeling elders is old in romance. Madeleine's feelings for Emile—as much the opening of love as of being in love with a dashing cavalier —were at work within her. That she had vowed to break her bad habits was its own sign. A young girl does not set out on self-reform unless she desires to find her reward in a loved one's eyes. Such intentions of reform fail to suggest a passing flirtation; it was beyond that.

She was an obstinate young woman, fond of her own way. Opposition, openly expressed at home, strengthened that obstinacy to the extent of overcoming the guidance of obedience and common sense.

Emile wrote fervently to her, if no record remains of what he said. Whatever views he expressed, they must have hardened her resolve. All thoughts of parting soon went. Within a few days of deciding so definitely the correspondence must "*stop*" she wrote from Row, on April 23:

> My dear Emile accept my thanks for your very kind and flattering note. You must have discovered that I have a great regard for you or I should not have acted as I have done—If I can promote your happiness in the least believe me I shall be most willing to do so
>
> > "Why should I blush to own I love"
> > "Tis love that rules the realm above"
> > "Why should I blush to say to all"
> > "That virtue holds my heart in thrall"
>
> Do not at present get an introduction to papa . . . now dear Emile all this must remain a profound secret—Mention my

name to no one. This I ask as a favour I shall depend on your honour . . .

And in the extravagance of her feelings she left three blank pages at the end of the letter, when, in nearly every future example, she filled every inch of the paper she used, and, worse, wrote crossways over the existing writing in the ugly Italian style then so popular.

Just under a month later she wrote even more warmly:

> My thoughts are often of you. I have often loved before but never have I loved one better than you—When I set my affections on any one I am true to them. I shall never be able to introduce you to Papa—It must be a stranger so how are we to manage it I dont know I have thought of it night and day . . . we must have patience. I practise my music every day— But I do not sing I only play duets with Bessie . . . Emile do not ask for a lock of my hair—Any other thing I will give you but not a lock of hair. I promised to one who is now in the cold grave I should never give a second lock of hair and a promise to the dead is sacred do not blame me refusing it *even* to you whom I love so dearly . . .

This promise, made to "that amusing Charles," her teen-age lover who died, is a rather sudden obedience to an almost forgotten affair. It could have been Madeleine becoming suddenly coy, in that unexpected feminine way.

They met secretly in several places. Emile has written of "walking in the woods" with her. This must have been the wooded country round Rowaleyn but that summer they were almost caught together. She wrote an agitated letter:

> My Beloved Emile Providence must be on our side or he would not have made us such wonderful escapes. Papa did not see you today—thank God he did not—I was very sorry we had not time to take a parting kiss—we shall make up for it next time . . .

Their devotion grew with such meetings. They contrived to defeat the watching world, speaking so boldly to each other that Emile, in the summer, told Mary Perry he was "engaged" to Madeleine Smith.

His letters home (these in particular do not exist but Elmire was to recall their fervour) were almost rhapsodies. He was in love and jubilant about it. Madeleine adored him; for the future he had bold plans, the expressions, perhaps, of a young man in the throes of ecstasy and passion.

Their feelings were gathering strength, their beings alight with the joy of each other.

The delirium had truly begun.

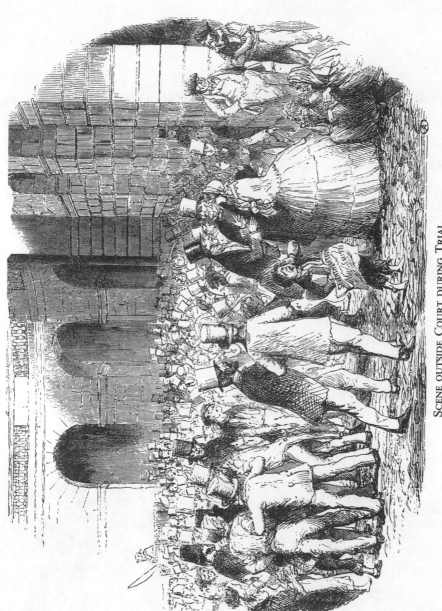

SCENE OUTSIDE COURT DURING TRIAL

(*Left*) EMILE L'ANGELIER
(Artist's copy made from
an existing portrait)

(*Right*) MADELEINE SMITH
IN THE DOCK
(A rare, recently discovered
water-colour by
William Brodie, R.S.A.)

Courtesy of A. Irvine Adams

MADELEINE SMITH

EMILE L'ANGELIER

(*Right*) L'ANGELIER'S LODGING
in Franklin Place

(Left)
MADELEINE SMITH'S GRAVE
(at Mount Hope Cemetery,
near New York City)

(Below) L'ANGELIER'S FAMILY TOMB IN JERSEY
(his name bottom of middle stone)

CHAPTER FIVE

The Burning Heart

*The flirtation developed into an intrigue, the changed
relations of the lovers being reflected in the tropical and
abandoned tone of the fair correspondent.*
William Roughead: *Mainly Murder.*

IT IS NOT always easy to assess the actions and behaviour of
people a century away. Madeleine's world is a curious, sometimes puzzling era despite Lytton Strachey's contention that
"the history of the Victorian Age will never be written
because we know too much about it."

In Madeleine's case she was brought up by the application
of rigid standards, guarded and protected as much as possible
from the realities and grossnesses of life. For all this, she
managed to develop her character and individuality within
the constricting walls of middle-class Victorianism.

She lived at a time of great contrasts, in a land of back-
ward ideas for all the surge of industrialisation. *The Times*
frequently warned its readers in admonitory leaders of "our
increasing worship of money."

Vice was rampant ("sexual anarchy" it was called). In
the year Madeleine first met Emile, the police recorded no
less than 5,000 arrests of disorderly prostitutes in London in
a twelvemonth; in one street naked women or women clad
only in shifts dragged passing men into brothels (the *Lancet*
claimed one London house in every sixty was a brothel and
one female in every sixteen a whore). It was not long before
the Rector of Marylebone Church declared England "the
most religious in pretension but in reality the most immoral
and licentious nation under the sun."

Scotland was not much better. There exists a picture of

49

the almost authoritarian Scots' Sabbath gloom in the famous story of an Edinburgh prostitute who drove a customer from her rooms because he refused to stop whistling on the Sabbath—exaggerated as the story may be, existing strictures gave rise to it.

About then the House of Commons rejected a bill to regulate the working hours in bleaching factories where young girls slaved for almost 20 hours a day in temperatures of up to 130 degrees; children under ten frequently shared such work.

Thousands of other girls worked 130 hours a week to earn 4d. an hour, buttonholing and sewing shirts. Misery was rampant and at least 80 per cent of the population had incomes of under £100 a year.

But in literature, as in superficial life, all was purity and sanctity to such an extent that a few years later the omnipotent Mr. Mudie, lord of the popular circulating libraries, put *The Ordeal of Richard Feverel* on his *index prohibitorum*. In lesser things a lady was fined for permitting her female servant to stand on a sill cleaning windows, to the danger of her life, so that "the public decency was shocked." Not until 1857 did Parliament, as a further example, begin debating a bill to set up a Court of Divorce.

For all these sorry pictures, it was also a time of rebellion in many fields, which neither church nor state could wholly stifle.

Madeleine, perhaps scenting this fever in the air, was preparing to stage her own resentment in a practical form against the moral laws which surrounded her own small life.

*　　　*　　　*

Emile was a prolific correspondent to his new love, but though she did not keep his letters for long they appeared to reach her safely, usually through poste restante in Glasgow or Row, under various noms-de-plume.*

---

* At pertinent times he also used a covering name for letters she addressed to Helensburgh post office; his pseudonym was Mr. M'Call.

Her own feelings for him were expressed in overwhelming terms with that tireless prolixity at which the Victorians excelled.

In July they had become secretly engaged and Mary Perry had, as she said, been the first to know of it.

The little spinster was his close confidante, and Emile enjoyed sharing his excitement. Being a most ardent lover it was essential he should be able to talk freely about Madeleine to someone he could trust.

But more than at the parental objections which seemed to lie ahead, he was disturbed about his prospects at Huggins and Company.

These were not bright. At his present rate of progress it would be years before he could marry. His anxiety to support a wife was genuine enough, and whatever later commentators have to say of his implied fortune-hunting, there was no truth in it. He wrote to Anastasie of wanting a place of his own, but "How?" *She* would have no money "I believe, and I have none."

In July and August the stolen meetings went on. He was now her "sweet Emile" and there were warmer endearments in her letters ("I never saw anyone I could love as I do you"). He desired her to meet his family and they laid plans to bring it about; nothing remains to show how it was proposed to forward such an idea. In July, too, she sent a warmly affectionate letter filled with love and much gossip in that fashion always peculiarly her own:

My own beloved Emile I hope and trust you arrived safe home on Monday. 1 did so enjoy your kind visit on Sunday— It makes me feel in good spirits for a week after seeing you. Oh I wish I could see you often it would be such a comfort to both of us—But I hope there is happiness in store for us yet. When we are married it will be my constant endeavour to please you and to add to your comfort. I shall try to study you and when you get a *little* out of temper I shall try and pet you dearest—kiss and fondly you. I was not astonished at you thinking me cool for I really have been in fault but it is my

way. But I must change it to you—I shall try and be more
affectionate for the future. You know I love you dearly—Ah
Emile you possess my love. I could not love any other as I do
you and believe me I shall ever remain true to you. I think a
woman who can be untrue ought to be banished from society
—It is a most heartless thing . . . After luncheon two gentlemen
my little brother James and myself went and had a walk of
7 miles across the hill to Loch Lomond. How often I wished
you had been with me I cannot tell—I do not enjoy any other
ones company but yours. Your likeness is such a comfort to
me Whenever I think of my dear Emile I go and look at you
I never saw such a good likeness I love it truly—I owe you
very many thanks for it—I shall try and get mine for you
before you leave—Tell me beloved if there is anything I can
do to please you Do tell me if you love me—B/ told me she
saw you—On Sunday one of the ladys in mamas carriage saw
you and fancy she fell in love with your appearence. I do not
wonder at that in the least—as I was quite charmed with you.
I do not wonder at young ladies admiring you

They exchanged portraits (the stilted but already out-
moded daguerreotypes of the period). Though exhibits at the
eventual trial, both these unique pictures completely vanished
and have no known duplicates.

From Jersey came news. Bernard Saunders, that invaluable
friend whose appreciation of Emile was always to be of the
warmest, was writing to a business friend in Glasgow.

A letter duly reached Emile from this friend, bidding him
to call. He did so and matters came up which promised well
for his future.

An assistant was needed on one of the many flourishing
market-gardens outside Lima, in Peru. There would be a
good salary, a house suitable for a white overseer of native
labour, and paid passages. Emile was in a condition of frantic
excitement about it, believing he had an excellent chance of
being chosen for the post. He wrote home begging that
Saunders, Uncle René, Uncle Jean de la Croix (Melanie's
only brother), and any other qualified person should write
forthwith to say how well qualified he was for the position.

Perhaps in the delight of such heady possibilities, he contrived the feat of personally conducting Madeleine to "dear Mary's" house on a visit in August. He wished his beloved to be seen (and approved) by his "best, kindest friend."

There, in Renfrew Street, their hearts must have poured out. The story of the dangers on the Smith front, the manner in which their clandestine correspondence was conducted, their great, overriding love—all these were surely revealed to sympathetic Mary Perry. Her sentimental mind was enraptured by so charming an affection. Young, penniless love; a fierce papa; secret letters; social distinctions; it was veritably a novel hand-made for Mr. Mudie's misty-eyed subscribers.

It was growing to be a consuming passion on both sides, extravagant in many ways but at least sincere. He was her precious Emile and she had chosen (or he had) a name she now used, "Mimi."* It is not known how this pet name came about. Had Madeleine heard of opera's tragic Mimi, who did not then "exist," the choice could have been her imagination at work. Emile used the name in addressing her, though never in letters home and seldom in referring to her.

She was instantly alarmed, when she learned of it, at the drawbacks of Lima. She was to emphasise her fears and distress at the very idea, but had found an adroit way round the promise to the dead, for "you shall have a lock of my hair. When I refused it at first we were not engaged—Now we are and you have a right to ask anything from me."

From his small savings, and from his mother, Emile got together the fare to Jersey. He had enough over to pay a brief, long-intended visit to Charles Lane, whose acquaintance he had made five years before on the summer holiday spent with the De Rosen family.

The Lanes, whose daughters became Emile's slaves, lived

* Sometimes she signed 'Minie,' an unhappy choice in those days, for it was the name of a then popular French explosive bullet (Minié) of considerable destructive power and current cant for anything comparable to those powers (at home Madeleine received her full name, but Bessie often called her 'Lena' which Mr. Smith disliked).

in a big house at Badgemore, just outside Henley-on-Thames; on his arrival there a letter was waiting from Madeleine:

My dearest Emile, I left you very sad indeed what if I should never see you the more. Oh Emile the thought is dreadful for my sake take care of yourself. Your Mimi shall pray for you the night—You shall be my constant thought. I do feel so happy that I know your dear friend Miss P I like her very much—I do not wonder at your loving her as you do . . . I have been thinking about telling Papa—But I know he would get into a passion and would not listen to a word. You cannot fancy what a dislike he has to you his reasons I do not know—He would tell me to put a stop to all intercourse—He would try and break our engagement (but death only shall break that engagement with me) Never shall I take anyone but my own dear Emile and call me their wife. Whatever occurs I shall remain true true to the last—I love you too much ever to cheat you . . . write me before you leave England (address it care of Haggart James Smith—Roualeyn, Row and put a small M in the corner) Do not write in your usual hand in case of Bessie taking it out of the Post Bag . . .

Emile was on a belated summer holiday from Huggins. His journey to Jersey included both a plan of talking about Lima at a family council, and a desire to commiserate over Achille's death; the last motive was a strong one. Emile's roots went deep.

Melanie Langelier was only fifty-four then, but was aged before her time. She found life hard and the burden of caring for the shop weighed heavily on her. Pierre; Zephirine; Achille; Claude—they had all gone and, in a sense, so had Emile.

But when he arrived she was delighted. If he had not changed a lot since they last met, he was decidedly more mature and showed the signs of a sense of responsibility.

He seemed genuinely in love and aware of the vital requirement of steadying his life. He was thirty-two now, and like many men of a casual, irresponsible outlook, found love brought him up against reality with a jerk.

Jersey, for him, had not changed very much. Anastasie was helping Melanie with the shop, while Elmire had that year celebrated her twenty-first birthday: they staged a second small festivity so he could share in it. But first, to please Melanie, he went with her to Green Street Cemetery to see Achille's name on the squat family gravestone towards the end of the long burial ground.

It was almost like the old days at Library Place. Moved by his fondness for his mother, and perhaps the pleasure of being in love, Emile was like the person he had been before he left the island.

He poured out his plans for Lima, and ran into his mother's stark terror.

Not only did the sound of Peru frighten her, but she had read in the newspaper of President Ramón Castilla's accession after the savage revolt against the corrupt government of Echenques. It was too soon for the brief period of prosperity and peace brought by Castilla to be generally known; Peru, to outsiders, was still a bloody, dreadful land.

That Emile lived in Scotland she could endure, but begged him not to consider Peru.

*   *   *

With unconscious timing a letter arrived from Madeleine at Row. She was hastening to emphasise her dislike of Lima:

My Dearest Emile—How I long to see you. It looks an age since I bid you adieu . . . I do not intend to say anything till I have seen you—I shall be guided by you entirely and who could be a better guide to me than my intended husband? I hope you have given up all idea of going to Lima—I will never be allowed to go to Lima with you—so I shall fancy you want to be quit of your Mimi. You can get plenty of appointments in Europe and place in Europe. For my sake dont go . . . We are very gay this week I am quite tired of company—What I would not give to be with you alone—Oh would we not be happy. Ah happy as the day was long . . . I feel very nervous today My hand shakes so. I have not felt well since I got your last letter and I try to appear cheerful before my family and it is not easy to appear in good spirits when there is a pain at the heart—It will break my heart if you go away. You dont know how I love you Emile I live for you alone. I adore you. I could never love another as I do you—Oh dearest Emile would I might clasp you now to my heart. Adieu for today if I have time I shall write another note—before I post this . . . So adieu dearest love and a fond embrace—Believe me your ever devoted and fond

MIMI

Tuesday morning

Beloved Emile I have dreamt all night of you I hope you are well. How you must be enjoying yourself with all your dear kind friends. Have you met many young ladies since you have been away. We have most delightful weather . . . I am most anxious to receive your next Letter—I am in too low spirits to write so adieu dearest—May God bless and prosper you. *A kiss.* Your true fond

MIMI

It was an untidy, devoted outpouring. In other letters at the same time she was to repeat her fears, and how so great a distance would part them for good. She played a deft card in drawing her loved one's attention to the dangers of the climate, "for I am sure you will not live for more than three or four years if you go" and in another letter, "Will the day ever come when you shall call me Wife—Alas if you go to Lima . . ."

Melanie saw the letters. In maternal fears any ally is worth having. It is obvious she used Madeleine's worry as moral support. Elmire said nothing (though later was to express a view the job would have been the making of her brother); Anastasie supported her mother. Saunders wisely put forth no more than token views.

The family council (grandmother de la Croix; René; cousin Edouard Langelier, and Jean de la Croix) saw Melanie's fright at the prospect. The outcome was a letter to Madeleine at Row post office. The plan was abandoned. Emile had some definite regrets about it, but never mentioned them again and behaved admirably, parting happily from Melanie when he returned to Glasgow.

Madeleine, in a flurry of gratitude that there was no danger of her being transported to South America, got down to the troublesome problem of facing James Smith with the story of her love, and how she desired above all else to marry Emile. It took real courage on her part. For all her bold, self-indulgent spirit, and her highly practical outlook on life, fear of the grim Victorian paterfamilias required quelling in order to offer defiance. She was a minor, a girl, and without means. Hedonism was an enjoyable cult; facing the head of the family on his own ground in defence of it was too big a task for Madeleine.

James would not for one minute tolerate her nonsense; his eyes (grey like hers, but "very direct and stern") must have been formidable. The interview was a violent one, conducted by a father whose eldest child matched him in temper and who was not afraid to stand *almost* on her own feet.

The discussion was held at Rowaleyn, taking in the whole family. The scene was noisy, for Madeleine had personal courage and the recklessness of being in love to sustain her, even though she wrapped up the truth and diplomatically softened the edges of facts.

What James said is not known. His character is defined enough to guess he would have stood solidly against an impecunious nobody, a foreigner, and, not at all unlikely, a Catholic—Jane Street was no more than camouflage on this worst sin of all. To a staunch Protestant in 1855, Catholicism was loathsome. To be a Papist born was something no transfer of religious faith could nullify. The order went out that any thought of even considering the match was out of question.

Madeleine rushed to her bedroom and wrote to Emile in tones of passionate drama, and signed it with her proper name to lend force to the message:

Farewell Dear Emile

A last fond farewell—My Papa will not give his consent. I have given my word of honour I will have no more communi-

cation with you ... Get married—You will never get one who
will love you as I have done. I must banish your image from
my heart—It almost breaks my heart to return to you your
likeness and chain—I must not keep them—Write me a parting
note The last one I can ever receive. Go—go to Lima may
God protect you is my prayer. As a parting favour may I ask
that you will burn all my letters the day you receive this do it.
Adieu I shall never see you again No never. Be happy—forget
me and may she whom you call your wife be a comfort unto
you. May she love and esteem you—Fare thee well

MADELEINE—

There was a sad letter written to Mary Perry at the same
time, to make doubly sure the truth was brought home to
Emile:

Dearest Miss Perry—Many kind thanks for all your kindness. Emile will tell you I have bid him adieu—My Papa would
not give his consent so I am in duty bound to obey him.
Comfort dear Emile—It is a very heavy blow to us both.
I had hoped some day to have been happy with him but alas
it was not intended—we were doomed to be disappointed. You
have been a kind friend to him—Oh Continue so. I hope and
trust he may prosper in the step he is about to take—I am glad
now that he is leaving this country for it would have caused me
great pain to meet him. Think my conduct not unkind—I have
a father to please and a kind father too—Farewell dear Miss
Perry and with much love believe me yours most sincerely—

MIMI

Either Emile was too overcome to deal with such a sudden
ending of his romance and his hopes, or, which is highly
probable, he did not know how to get in touch with her
immediately. In any case, he does not appear to have sent
an answer. Existing is an undated letter which can only fit in
at this and no other point in their lives:

dearest Emile
    For the love of heaven write to me if it should only be a line
—I know you must hate me—But oh forgive me—Write by
return Post—No one shall know—Perhaps papa has written

you (I know not) telling you never more to write to me. He shall never know—I have suffered much. It cant be helped—Hope we may yet be happy—love yours

MIMI—

A draft of a letter was later found in Emile's hand which was obviously an answer to Madeleine's own explanations and farewells.

It bears a July date (in the middle of the writing) though the draft is undated. Emile was clearly using an old sheet of paper on which to record his notes and duly sent, it can be assumed, a clarified version to Madeleine. Such bluntness is unexpected and yet, as subsequent events will show, only a moment's darkness on the sunny waters:

In the first place I did not deserve to be treated as you have done. How you astonish me by writing such a note without descending to explain the reasons why your father refuses his consent. He must have reasons, and I am not allowed to clare myself of accusations.

I should have written you before, but I preferred awaiting untill I got over the surprise your last letter caused me and also to be able to write you in a calm and collected manner, free from any animosities whatever.

Never, dear Madeleine, could I have believed you were capable of such conduct. I thought and believed you unfit for such a step. I believed you were true to your word and to your *honour*. I will put questions to you which answer to yourself. What would you think if even one of your servants had played with any one's affections as you have done, or what would you say to hear that any lady friends had done what you have —or what am I to   of you now? What is your opinion of your own self after those solemn vows you uttered and wrote to me. Shew my letters to any one, Madeleine, I don't care who, and if any find I mislead you I will free you from all blame. I warned you repeatedly not to be rash in your engagement and vows to me, but you persisted in that false and deceitful flirtation, playing with affections which you knew to be pure and undivided, and knowing at the same time that at a word from your father you would break all your engagement.

You have deceived your father as you have deceived me. You never told him how solemnly you bound yourself to me, or if you had, for the honour of his daughter he could not have asked to break of an engagement such as ours. Madeleine, you have truly acted wrong. May this be a lesson to you never to trifle with any again. I wish you every happiness. I shall be truly happy to hear you are happy with another. You desire and now you are at liberty to recognise me or cut me just as you wish—but I give you my word of honour I shall act always as a Gentleman towards you. We may meet yet, as my intentions of going to Lima are now at an end. I would have gone for your sake. Yes I would have sacrificed all to have you with me and to leave Glasgow and your friends you detested so very much. Think what your father would say if I sent him your letters for a perusal. Do you think he could sanction your breaking your promises. No, Madeleine, I leave your conscience to speak for itself.

I flatter myself he can only accuse me of a want of fortune. But he must remember he too had to begin the world with dark clouds round him.

I cannot put it into my mind that yet you are at the bottom of all this.

It is the hurt, angry outpouring of a baffled lover. Not until later did he learn something of James's objections, and Madeleine's farewell naturally sparked off the answer; she said all the wrong things in the wrong way. The male in love is more sensitive than a girl in his reaction to imagined or implied slights, in his ability to read into innocent expressions the indications of feminine cunning. From this letter springs the first belief in Emile's blackmailing ideas; such a charge does not stand, for the threat of "showing" her letters is no more than spite and bitterness.

His letter is neither kind nor understanding, written under the drive of anger that one so close should cross him. The version he must have sent doubtless contained more caution; people who flee to the pen (and are not able in its use) write from the heart, with unhappy results.

It is a not indifferent slant on Emile's character. His

native good sense would have seen to it the finished letter was more circumspect; the actual process of re-writing and revision would have been good modifiers. They must have been. All was well again and Madeleine's letters were soon pouring on him again—adoring, passionate, indiscreet.

They were meeting afresh, tokens had been exchanged and she was even the careless Madeleine once more as when she wrote him a long letter, adding a coquettish postscript:

> I lost the ring while I was walking with you yesterday. It must have slipped out of my pocket I dont care for the ring only I intended to wear it because you had worn it—you will say I am a very naughty careless thing—love MIMI—

The loss could have been the sequel to an invitation she sent him on November 10 in which she explained about a bad cold lasting "for a week but I feel a little better—I am going to walk to Helensburgh how happy I could feel if I could have you to accompany me . . . I can walk 5 miles without a rest . . . I hope you are free from your cough." This was posted on a Saturday morning; Emile may have received it in time to rush off by rail or steamer in order to catch her on the walk.

*   *   *

At home for some time Madeleine was on sufferance. Her father had expressed his views, and, as on that grim Barrett hearth in Wimpole Street ten years before, he required them to be observed and obeyed; that was the whole of it. The thought of disobedience would never have occurred to him.

He also voiced his wishes to his wife. It was therefore her duty to see that nobody—and no letters—slipped past the parental barricade either in India Street or at Rowaleyn. It was no more than a matter of arrangement to avoid the obstacle in Glasgow.

The morning post arrived just after 7.30 and was taken in by the housemaid, Christina Haggart. Letters from Emile were addressed to her with Madeleine's initial in one corner.

The girl was Madeleine's ally, the more so because she was enamoured of a young carpenter named Mackenzie. The Smith household had its own views about followers—which did not worry Jean Craig, the elderly cook, or Alison, the married tablemaid—and Madeleine was therefore helpful in the matter of concealment for the below-stairs' lovers.

Christina had only joined them the previous April. She had at once taken to Madeleine and it was due to her freedom as a servant the prolific correspondence was maintained. It was Christina who often undertook the posting of letters to Emile when out on various errands; at Row she was also invaluable, for though envelopes usually went to the combined general store and post office, addressed to "Miss Bruce" or "Miss Richard," the maid invariably collected them.

Mrs. Smith took her opinions from her husband. If Emile was not to be countenanced, she saw it was so, but so guileless and innocent a mother could do no more than offer opinions. Her only positive action was in ordering Christina to bring all letters for her scrutiny which, since forbidden ones had already been removed, amounted to nothing.

Bessie was in blunt opposition to Emile and could no longer be relied on ("B/ is much changed in her manner for the worse . . . B and I do not agree at all so we have little conversation"). This could have been due to spite or envy. Madeleine was the successful, the bold one, and though Bessie was the prettier of the pair it was Madeleine who received all the attention from men of any age who visited them (one overcome old gentleman made valiant attempts to kiss Madeleine at Rowaleyn). Bessie was never to marry and it could be that her rooted objections to Emile were unconscious manifestations of incipient spinsterhood—that was to come. Just then it appears Madeleine had to "do all I can to prevent my sister being fast."

Nor was Jack Smith much better, hanging round the house awaiting the time when he was to go to work in an accountant's office in Ingram Street. Of the family, he was actually

the closest to Madeleine, understanding her better than any
of them; his opinion was that Emile was only a "clerk" and
was thus socially and financially unacceptable. The children
naturally did not count. Little brown-haired Janet was only
eleven, a self-contained child not given to showing affection
for anyone, while James, a small boy of nine, never did appeal
to Madeleine.

Despite opposition the lovers contrived many secret meetings. How they managed it is a tribute to their unfailing
determination and ingenuity; they were talking definitely of
marriage and had settled in their minds the importance of
the ceremony taking place, somehow and soon. Madeleine
was half prepared to brave family wrath.

There exist several letters from her making this clear, yet,
in some way, the phraseology suggests a form of lip-service.
It was not so much insincere as uneasy, inserted at frequent
intervals in long passages of gossip as if reassuring herself as
much as Emile.

A letter written in December expresses her alarm at one
of Emile's frequent colds. It addresses him as "my own
darling husband" and goes on to say:

> I think you should consult Dr M'Farlan—that is go and see
> him get him to sound you—ask him to prescribe for you and
> tell you what is wrong with you—if you have any love for your
> Mimi follow his advice and oh sweet love do not try and Dr
> yourself be good for once and I am sure you will be well. Is it
> not horrid cold weather. I did my love so pity you standing in
> the cold last night but I could not get Janet to sleep little stupid
> thing. This is a horrid scroll as I have been stoped twice with
> that bore visiter—My own sweet beloved I can say nothing as
> to our marriage as it is not certain when they may go from
> home or when I may go to Edr it is uncertain—My beloved will
> we require to be married if it is in Edr or will it do here? You
> know I know nothing of these things I fear the Banns in Glas-
> gow there are so many people know me—If I had any other
> name but Madeleine it might pass but it is not a very common
> one—But we must manage in some way to be united ere we
> leave Town—How kind of Mary to take any trouble with us

she must be a dear good creature. I would like to visit her but no I cannot—I shall never forget the first visit I paid with my own beloved husband my own sweet dear Emile—you sweet dear darling. If ever I again I show temper which I hope to God I wont dont mind it it is not with you I am cross—Sweet love I adore you with my heart and soul I must have a letter from you soon.

The pair managed, with reckless daring, to spend stolen hours together from time to time at the beginning of 1856 in the laundry at India Street and, on two occasions, the drawing-room, after the family had retired.

These meetings were sometimes happy and sometimes stormy. Emile's morality, neither better nor worse than the young men of the time, so far aroused no warm response from Madeleine, passionate as her feelings were ("I shall not yield to you—you shall marry me pure and innocent as the day on which I was born—You shall never deprive me of my honour—I shall be firm on this point dearest").

Emile's desire could have been no more ardent than the typical hunger for the beloved which young men regard as a correct prelude to the legality of marriage. He did not exert more than the usual form of persuasion dressed up in romantic phrases; it was almost as if he was doing what was expected of him since he failed to make any remarkable efforts to achieve his object. Madeleine's resistance was slightly melodramatic, the gestures of the girl who might be willing to yield but at her own time and place, after a prolonged period of consideration and steady reluctance.

More than one commentator had seen in Emile L'Angelier the plottings of the expert foreign seducer filled with deft stratagems devised to steal Madeleine's virginity and, so to speak, wreak on her his own vile lusts.

It is a farcical picture, quite out of focus. Emile knew perfectly well her physical hunger matched his own. On his part it was the typical need of the male animal and about as subtle, while she had the strong defences proper to women who are determined for things to go exactly as they wish.

In those days virginity was the automatic requirement in unmarried women, and far more than now they had the pitiless code of the times to sustain them. The weaklings might go to the wall, while Madeleine never showed weakness in her whole life. It takes two people to complete a seduction. The notion of the maiden swooning before the tide of irresistible passion and being carried helplessly along by it may appeal to novelists; it also docs to women who need an excuse to explain their own shortcomings, or to cover them up.

Madeleine, in her letters alone, was an inflammatory young woman. If Emile got caught up by this there can be no excuse for him, not that it makes him any the worse than the rest of his sex in similar circumstances.

For the moment the lovers had the winter to pass through; concupiscence, like most natural things, is usually speeded to fruition by the sun and soft winds of spring and summer.

CHAPTER SIX

The Woods of Rowaleyn

*Upon a May evening, when blood fell on the anemone and
the compact of tragedy was sealed and signed.*

Sacheverell Sitwell: *Splendours and Miseries.*

ALL THOUGHTS OF another job had left Emile L'Angelier.
If he was worried about how to secure his future and achieve
marriage, he showed no visible signs of it.

His social life, when he was not seeing Madeleine or
writing to her, continued as it always had. Much of his time
was spent with August de Mean, the Chancellor of the French
Consulate, who was not so much an intimate friend as one
who understood the workings of his native temperament in
others, particularly when the Gascon in Emile happened to
be uppermost.

Though the Consul, Mauboussin, lived above the official
establishment in West George Street with some of his staff,
de Mean had his own town lodging. Just before Emile made
the trip to Jersey, de Mean moved to Helensburgh, a thirty-
minute train journey from Glasgow.

Emile sometimes made a habit of going there. Row was
only two miles away and this could have been part of the
attraction. He did not use it as an actual base for visiting
Madeleine, but obviously hoped to meet her by chance—he
often accompanied de Mean on local walks. Helensburgh
had another advantage in being a perfectly legitimate destination which Emile could mention generally and aloud, when,
indeed, he secretly planned to go on to Rowaleyn.

De Mean was a most unwilling audience for Emile's
stories of his love, confidences the anxious swain had to
impart to some one. The other man did not share with Mary

Perry the enjoyment of a passive role; he sustained it only out of the kindness he felt in common with others towards Emile.

The intrigue cut right across de Mean's practical outlook and trained bureaucratic mind. He detested subterfuge and knew only too well the dangers underlying rigid paternal objections. He warmly urged his friend to have done with pretence and bring the affair into the open, to seek James Smith's consent and, perhaps, blessing.

This was clearly impossible, and Emile knew it. Smith had spoken and such was his nature he would have permitted no further reference to be made to a meeting between them. For any one to return to a matter he regarded as closed and settled would not only have been folly, but an invitation to incite his furious temper.

It has been wondered why Emile never made a direct approach. He often passed 124 St. Vincent Street; the visit could have been simply accomplished. But Madeleine's statement that "he hates you with all his heart—he despises you" was no encouragement for a poor and humble lover. Fiction abounds in brash Lochinvars who have stormed terrifying fathers in their lairs; Emile was a lower-class nobody in Victorian Scotland, and not endowed with much courage.

Again, James Smith was too important to be stormed. He was a leading citizen, a rich and successful man. At St. Vincent Street he was the tenant of his most intimate friend, John Houldsworth, head of a wealthy firm of cotton spinners and a director of many insurance companies, Vice-Commodore of the fashionable Northern Yacht Club and a Baillie of the City Council.

Third in this trilogy of close companions was the Hon. Andrew Orr, of the big wholesale and export stationers, Francis Orr and Sons, and, above all, Lord Provost of Glasgow.

Against Smith and his friends, of which Houldsworth was one of the richest men in Glasgow and the other its civic head, L'Angelier would not have lasted for minutes, had he

openly tackled Smith and turned his dislike into active
retaliation. Discretion was the wisest policy for the moment,
quite apart from Madeleine's almost hysterical anxiety that
her lover should make no open move.

*   *   *

Her letters continued, each one consciously addressed in
a different hand but, with futile carelessness, in the tiny cream
envelopes she always used, distinguished by a meaningless
embossed device of oak-leaves-and-apples on the flaps.

These letters were on a bewildering assortment of papers
of every shape, shade, and quality; some were on a tissue-
thin mauve paper heavily inscribed on both sides in thick
ink. At times she revealed a strange patriotism by using
paper dye-stamped in bright colours, showing the Union
Flag and the Tricolour crossed on an anchor, with a scroll
in black capital letters: "May they ever remain united."
Perhaps she saw this as a *double entente* piously directed both
at international amity, and herself and Emile.

She was still receiving her letters through Christina Haggart to avoid their detention. The family was behaving in the
deliberate manner of people desiring to damp the eldest
child's ardour, only to fan it to greater heat by such tactics.
Mrs. Smith openly announced she hated Emile, watching
every move Madeleine tried to make ("Mama would indeed
see me dead than beloved your wife").

James Smith was no less vehement. He was even in a
"great state of excitement" for days after Emile had innocently passed the door of 124 St. Vincent Street on his
normal occasions. Bessie's dislike was shared by brother Jack:

> He came to sit with me tonight in my Bedroom—and he was
> telling me all the news he knew. I said I wish you would tell
> me some thing about a person the only person I love—L'Ange-
> lier he said. I was in fun I said No—well he said I am ashamed
> of you—do you know he is only a clerk in Huggins. I said I
> knew that but if I love him then that was enough—He tried
> to tell me I was expected to marry a rich man not a poor one—

He got a little cross and told me not to think of you as he knew P/ would be angry very angry.

If anything Madeleine's feelings were stimulated, if it was possible, in the natural manner of the female—passion and maternity in equal control—who sees in a despised follower the qualities of a martyred Galahad. She doted on everything about Emile and never hesitated to admit him to India Street at propitious moments.

On one occasion she contrived to send out the servants when the family was not at home and, with Christina Haggart's aid, Emile was to "come in by the back door which I shall order to be opened for you and we shall spend an hour and a half of happiness."

In her letters she openly exulted at "being *fondeled* by you" and while no real intimacy at that stage took place, the fiery Emile and his beloved may have indulged in familiarities reprehensible in the unmarried, but quite understandable in an age when single men and women were kept so rigidly apart that once they were together in privacy their love-making included every facet of behaviour short of sexual intercourse. The absurdities of forced restraint were revealed in moments when it could be avoided or circumvented. Victorian life, shot through with secret licence, never showed its faults so clearly as in the implacable separation of the sexes. Added to the delight of the lovers in by-passing such imposed barriers, Madeleine was frankly sensual, regarding Emile as her husband as he considered her his wife, a form of avowed alliance into which they had drifted and now saw as fact.

In the periods between moments of love they gave much attention to the serious question of official marriage. She wrote early in 1856 of how they would live together:

> I am sure we shall get on very well—with economy and though we had a *little one* yet it would cause vy vy little expense so I think we need not fear—I cannot understand why Miss P thinks it easier to do house keeping for a large family than for a small one—I think you and I would be so easily managed.

Do you think so—I would so like to be in your lodgings for a
week unknown to you just to see how you get on so that I
might do just the same when we go together—I shall not know
one thing you like or dislike—It shall be a little difficult at
first but remember darling I shall trust to you telling me all
these little things at the very first—You must begin with me as
you intend to end—Give me a good *blow up* whenever you have
a *little time* or nothing *else* to do beloved.

Meetings were planned with the caution of a cloak-and-
dagger drama: "You shall come to India St. half past ten
go to the opposite side I shall open the curtain of the drawing
room window—If I do not then come over to the door and
if all is clear I shall have it open." With true audacity she
scribbled this at the breakfast table under the eye of her
father, who presumed her preparing a shopping list.

The public declaration of the banns seemed to be the
insurmountable obstacle to an official marriage. This was
not helped when Mrs. Smith suddenly exhibited an unexpected firmness of character with her wayward daughter on
her return from a brief visit to Edinburgh:

... what a lecture I have had. I can not tell you dearest what
I have suffered this night—Emile I was told by Mama (Papa
is not at home knows nothing of it) that she knew Papa would
rather see me in my grave ah my grave than dearest your wife
I was told you were poor and but a clerk and that I should
look higher—You were called all that was bad I asked for
proofs—She told me I should never be your wife with their
consent—I said I intended to be your wife Nothing would
change me—I told her of the love I bore you she said she was
ashamed to hear me say I loved you—She wept she begged of
me to give you up—I was firm—I said never anothers would
I be—I said as soon as I was of age I would have my letters to
the house She said if I was some heiress I might talk that way
but my letters I would not have. Also that she would take care
the Post Man did not give me my letters at the Post Office—
She thinks I got them at the PO last year while at Row She
told me the anger of Papa would be fearful even she would be
afraid of it She implored me with Tears to give you up—It

cut me to see my Mother so—I felt I owed her my life I love
you I love her But the love for you rises far above the love for
her—Oh Emile husband have pity on your Mimi I suffered
much this night—I could not bear to hear her speak against
you My dearest my only love—I thought when I told her of
my love for you that would make her feel for me But alas
the Cold-ness of this World—I am never to be allowed out by
myself all this summer—Dearest I feel ill this night oh would
to God that you were here with me—Oh to comfort me to
cheer me in my distress—she said I often came into the Breakfast room like as if I had never been in Bed—the Picture of
unhappiness—she knew not the cause—But this explained all
She had no suspicion of me till B/ came from Edg and told her
she had seen you there—Then she thought you must have
known I was there—she has given me till after I come back
from Edg to fix what is to be the end of this. Husband dearest
one thing I shall propose I know you wont like it But I must
do something to have a little peace and happiness—Would
you consent to drop our correspondence till Sept When we
shall be married—You must think this cool of me But if you
wish me to live—I must have some happiness—If I continue
to correspond I shall be dead with misery ere Sept. This is a
horrid plan but darling what must I do can you trust me till
then the time shall pass quick—Emile I shall be thine in Sept.
God Knows I shall never be the wife of another After our
freedom how could I—No never. I am your wife.

The ultimatum, if it can be called that, was transitory. Out
of it came a brief tiff, with coldness on Emile's side (started,
quite obviously, by the possibility of no more letters for a
time). This was soon forgotten in a new flood of missives—
the loquacity of Madeleine's thoughts was equalled by her
speeding pen. She could write, almost day after day, long
letters filled with love, with serious sentiments interspersed
with domestic details. At times her handwriting and her
grammar were baffling (she usually scorned punctuation,
sharing with Edith Thompson, that other famous correspondent, a mania for dashes); at times her words were unreadable.

How Emile managed to decipher every line—if he did—is
difficult to understand. Possibly he skipped the inessentials
in search of each new scare or minor crisis he must have
come to expect as almost routine.

But in all that went on she did not forget his birthday on
April 30:

> My own my beloved Emile—I wrote to you on Sunday night
> for you to get my note on your birth day (today) but I could
> not get it posted. Disappointment it was to me But better late
> than never. My beloved may you have very very many happy
> returns of this day and each year may you find yourself happier
> than the last I trust darling that on your next birth day I may
> be with you to wish you many happy returns in person May
> you dearest have a long life—My constant prayer shall be your
> welfare and continued good health—I hope you continue to
> feel better My cough is a little better sometimes quite away and
> on cold days it comes back—On Sunday was I was at church
> and in the afternoon Jack and I had a walk of FOUR miles
> Now when I could walk 4 with a brother I could walk 8 with
> my own beloved husband and not be fatigued P/ is not at all
> well and very cross and he wont go to bed and get better So I
> tell him he deserves to be ill . . . Dearest how I picture our
> marriage day Where would you like to go the day we are
> married I dont fancy a place in particular so you can fix that
> when the time comes I hope it may yet turn out Sept. I asked
> P/ if I were to be married if the banns would be in Row Church
> And he said No I had nothing to do with the Row parish—
> I did not belong to it So darling it would not require to be here
> it would not do—I dont in the least mind if they wont give
> their consent for I know very well they shall be the first to give
> in . . . Kindest warmest love to you my husband dear a kiss
> another Oh to be in thy embrace my sweet Emile—Love again
> to thee from thy very fond thy loving and ever devoted Mimi
> —Thine
>
> OWN WIFE—

She referred to finding a box she had not opened for
"three years" and discovering within a notebook containing
several references to Emile. This does not make sense. It was

but a year since she had first known him (she wrote more than once of it). Possibly in her enthusiasm for the love affair either veracity or imagination had run away with her remembrance for dates.

*   *   *

A letter of May 3, 1856, indicates the eve of the consummation of their "marriage"; the assignation reads:

My own my beloved Emile—The very thought of seeing you so soon makes me feel happy and glad. Oh to hear you again speak to me—call me your own wife and to tell me that you love me. Can you wonder that I feel happy I shall be so happy to see you I cannot tell how I long to see you—It looks such an age since I saw you my sweet pet. I am well Cold quite gone. P/ has been in Bed two days If he should not feel well and come down on Tuesday it shall make no difference just you come—only darling I think if he is on the Boat you should get out at Helensburgh—Well beloved you shall come to the gate you know it and wait till I come. And then oh happiness wont I kiss you my love my own beloved Emile my husband dear. I dont think there is any risk Well Tuesday 6th May. The Gate half past 10 You understand darling I hope you are well—no cold Take care of yourself.

The family was now at Rowaleyn for the summer, where Madeleine's bedroom was on the ground floor giving direct access to the garden. It was in the grounds that the meeting took place. Sacheverell Sitwell poetically apotheosises the event in *Splendours and Miseries*, calling on romantic prose to lift their meeting into rarefied spheres:

. . . the early summer night, at half past ten.
The hour is come.
He sees a grey form, only her dress and nothing recognisable of her but her shape, gliding towards him along the grass edge of the path, under the trees. And she unlatches the gate for him, which he could have done himself, and takes him in. In that moment they are in each other's arms. The gear of time alters. They are now in the shadow of the trees, and sitting at

the tree foot, where no one can see or hear them. Here, their compact was signed, for we will call it that, a compact of tragedy . . .

It is not known how long the idyll lasted, or how long he stayed with her beneath the trees, their spring greenery occasionally lighted by the moon's first quarter, when it broke the clouds.

Either it must have been a considerable time and she did not sleep or, after such an epochal event, she rose early and in the chill, sunny brilliance of the morning wrote to Emile an impassioned note which contained a frankness almost surprising in a modern girl's correspondence. In 1856 it was startling:

> Wednesday Morning 5 o/c
> My own my beloved husband—I trust to God you got home safe and were not much the worse for being out. Thank you my love for coming so far to see your Mimi It was truly a pleasure to see you my Emile—Beloved if we did wrong last night it was in the excitement of our love—Yes beloved I did truly love you with my soul—I was happy it was a pleasure to be with you Oh if we could have remained never more to have parted But we must hope the time shall come—I must have been very stupid to you last night But every thing goes out of my head when I see you my darling my love . . . Beloved we shall wait till you are quite ready—I shall see and speak to Jack on Sunday I shall consider about telling Mama But I dont see any hope from her I know her mind—You of course cannot judge of my parents You know them not—I did not know or I should not have done it that I caused you to pay extra Postage for my stupid cold letters it shall not occur again. Darling Emile did I seem cold to you last night Darling I love you Yes my own Emile love you with my heart and soul. Am I not your wife Yes I am—And may you rest assured after what has passed I cannot be the wife of any other but dear Emile— No now it would be a sin . . . They cannot keep us from each other No that they never shall. Emile beloved I have sometimes thought would you not like to go to Lima after we are married? Would that not do Any place with you pet—I did not bleed in the least last night but I had a good deal of pain during the

night. Tell me pet were you angry at me for allowing you to do what you did was it very bad of me—We should I suppose have waited till we were married—I shall always remember last night Will we not often talk of our evening meetings after we are married—Why do you say in your letter—If we are *not* married I would not regret knowing you. Beloved have you a doubt but that we shall be married some day. I shall write to dear Mary soon—What would she say if she knew we were so intimate lose all her good opinion of us both would she not . . . Adieu again my husband God bless you and make you well And may you yet be very very happy with your Mimi as your little wife—Kindest love fond embrace and kisses from thy own true and ever devoted Mimi—Thy faithful

WIFE.

The court, at the eventual trial, was too shocked to permit this letter to be read in full; it was not in fact published until modern times.

Almost by return came an answer from Emile. His very long letter, one commentator has remarked, "suggests more of the adolescent prig than a man of the world." If Madeleine was frank, Emile was equally so:

My dearest and beloved wife Mimi,

Since I saw you I have been wretchedly sad. Would to God we had not met that night—I would have been much happier. I am sad at what we did, I regret it very much. Why, Mimi, did you give way after your promises? My pet it is a pity. Think of the consequences if I were never to marry you. What reproaches I should have, Mimi. I shall never be happy again. If ever I meet you again, love, it must be as at first. I will never again repeat what I did until we are regularly married. Try your friends once more—tell your determination—say nothing will change you, that you have thought seriously of it, and on that I shall firmly fix speaking to Huggins for Sept. Unless you do something of that sort, Heaven only knows when I shall marry you. Unless you do dearest I shall have to leave the country; truly dearest. I am in such a state of mind I do not care if I were dead. We did wrong. God forgive us for it Mimi, we have loved blindly. It is your parents fault if shame is the result, they are to blame for it all.

I got home quite safe after leaving you but I think it did my cold no good. I was fearfully excited the whole night. I was truly happy with you my pet, too much so for now I am too sad. I wish from the bottom of my heart we had never parted. Though we have sinned ask earnestly God's forgiveness and blessings that all the obstacles in our way be removed from us. I was disappointed my love at the little you had to say but I can understand why. You are not stupid, Mimi, and if you disappoint me in information, and I have cause to reproach you of it, you will have no one to blame but yourself, as I have given you warning long enough to improve yourself. Sometimes I do think you take no notice of my wishes and my desires but say yes for a mere matter of form. Mimi unless Huggins helps us I cannot see how I shall be able to marry you for years. What misery to have such a future in ones mind. speak to your to brother, open your heart to him, and try and win his friendship. Tell him if he loves you to take your part . . . Mimi dearest you must take a bold step to be my wife. I entreat you pet, by the love you have for me, Mimi, do speak to your mother—tell her it is the last time you shall ever speak of me to her. You are right Mimi, you cannot be the wife of any one else than me. I shall ever blame myself for what has taken place. I never never can be happy until you are my own, my dear fond wife. Oh Mimi, be bold for once, do not fear them—tell them you are my wife before God. Do not let them leave you without being married, for I cannot answer what would happen. My conscience reproaches me for a sin that marriage can only efface . . . We must not be separated all next winter, for I know Mimi you will be as giddy as last. You will be going to public balls and that I cannot endure . . . I do not understand, my pet, your not bleeding, for every woman having her virginity must bleed. You must have done so some other time. Try to remember if you never hurt yourself in washing &c. I am sorry you felt pain. I hope pet you are better. I trust, dearest, you will not be ——. Be sure to tell me immediately you are ill next time, and if at your regular period. I was not angry at your allowing me, Mimi, but I am sad it happened. You had no resolution. We should have waited till we were married, Mimi. It was very bad indeed. I shall look with regret on that night. No nothing except our Marriage will efface it from my memory. Mimi, only fancy if it was known. My dear, my pet, you would be dishonoured and that by me! Oh why was I born, my pet? I dread lest some great obstacle prevents our marriage. If Mary did know it, what should you be in her eyes?

For Gods sake burn this, Mimi, for fear any thing happening to you, do dearest.

It shows the tangled reactions of a very confused young man, blowing hot and cold simultaneously, animated both by shame and disillusion as much as by the aftermath of his desire.

Like many men whose siege of the loved one's virtue has unexpectedly succeeded, he hastened to blame Madeleine almost more than himself; he also saw farther and dreaded the possibility of a child. Like the animal in Galen's dictum who is sad after intercourse, his sadness developed into a hangover of self-reproach and morbid imaginings.

That milestone in their lives arouses a sense of inquiry. Despite opinions to the contrary, a personal view is that Emile was perhaps a most inexperienced seducer—for all his fine airs he somehow suggests it was often Parisian braggadocio speaking, not a man of the world.

Some of his letters to his sisters, oblique as they were, create a sneaking feeling he talked at second-hand. His conquests were not hidden but the recital of them delineates a dabbler—a veritable dabbler—at love.

Nothing he said was concrete, as could be expected. There was a distinct immaturity about his hints, like the youth boasting of his physical prowess with only the knowledge of inept amours to guide him.

The assumption is that Emile was not a great lover, only a sadly indifferent rake who may have read a lot of books or listened to salacious tales but had little reality to guide him, and only the clumsy passion of the ploughboy behind him. Blind desire he may have had, to be matched by Madeleine's; the ignorance of both translated their hunger into the active deed which may have been legally accomplished, but was not so in medical fact, as may be seen.

* * *

They planned another early meeting beneath the trees of Rowaleyn; she wrote to him on May 20:

> I have just a few minutes to write ere this note must go. If convenient for you I could meet you on Thursday night as P/ and M/ are not to be at home—Top of the garden same hour But darling write a note so that I may get it on Thursday night Miss Bruce PO Row—Now if this is not suitable just dont come I shall dearly love to see you—My own beloved my own true fond Emile . . . Yours for ever Mimi your own true and devoted
>
> WIFE—

This arrangement he could not have kept but did so on the Saturday night of the same week.

She wrote to him on Sunday, May 25, a letter with a mysterious allusion, never qualified, which suggests they may have indeed fulfilled by growing familiarity an act which had not, it seems, previously taken place.

For all Madeleine's apparent knowlege, she was bewildered by evidence which should have been noticeable on that night of May 6, but which (as their previous letters show) had not been present, and had caused Emile's bafflement:

> My beloved my own darling Emile. Words can never express to you how truly glad I was to see you last night—My husband my own true husband I am your wife no one can separate us now—No never, nothing on earth could make me proof untrue to you—Nothing I could hear against you. I could forgive you all for I know you love your Mimi—I love you fondly truly last night I did burn with love but we were good we withstood all temptations . . . some day we may *love* without fear or trick—we shall then be happy . . .

The letter continued with praise for Christina Haggart, who had coffee ready for her, and then, suddenly, raises a question which goes strangely with her previous statement of being "good":

> Emile my love my own darling—would we could meet tonight —but soon I trust, when I got in last night I discovered several spots of blood in my clothes—why was that I wonder——

Because Madeleine at times was perfectly capable of deluding herself in her letters, and in using wishful thinking hard by confusion of actual events, the letter suggests the act of marriage. The judge at the trial was to question, "Can you be surprised after such letters . . . that on the sixth of May . . . he got possession of her person?" It may have been so in law and in a matter of degree. In its physiological aspect the later date may be correct.

*   *   *

Whatever the answer they were not only in their own minds married, but were physically so.

Madeleine gloried in it, in utter defiance of the nice precepts of her day. Emile presently accepted it, once his spell of morbid heart-burning was over.

He had always taken, in his few existing letters or the copies of them (and in the reflection of them shown in her answers), an attitude combining proprietorial husbandly guidance and the fears of an anxious lover. She delighted in submission with an eye, possibly sincere, on their future married state when sanctified by church and law.

Yet, for all the warmth of her letters, she never made a real, definitely forwarding move to such an attainment. He desired it, but was frustrated both by finance and circumstance; she paid lip-service to the ideal of coming into the open, nullifying such a step by various fears of hesitancies, or pleaded their great difficulties, to plunge, without punctuated break, into the miscellanea of domesticity. It betrayed either complete *naïveté* or a subconscious wish that nothing should be done before the world.

If Madeleine Smith was simple then she was very simple

indeed; if not, she was brilliantly adroit, and, much more possible, her ingenuousness was directed unconsciously by an able mind planning ahead for her and guiding each move of her life by means of a cunning manifested in faultless instinctive behaviour. In cohesive thought she may have been aware of none of this nor did she deliberately evolve any of it.

If her instinct was her guardian angel, and she seemed to obey it, she was in remarkably good hands.

CHAPTER SEVEN

"Dear Emile's Wife"

Complete intimacy once established between them, Madeleine lets loose the pagan side of her nature, which was perhaps its most admirable quality . . .
F. Tennyson Jesse: *Trial of Madeleine Smith.*

THE LOVE AFFAIR settled down to a certain degree of pedestrianism with Madeleine as prolific as ever in her vows of devotion.

Early in June she wrote a short note to Mary Perry, whose house was almost another home to Emile:

My Dearest Mary—A thousand thanks for your dear kind note and good wishes for my happiness—I hope there are many many happy days in store for us. I know I shall be happy with my dear Emile—We love each other and that shall constitute our happiness. I trust the day is not far distant when you shall see us living happily together. I had a conversation with Mama but I received no hope from her. She shall never consent to our marriage—I told her my mind was made up nothing would change me. I shall be the wife of dear Emile— I made him once very unhappy. But I vowed I would never do so again by breaking my vows to him—Dear Mary nothing I fear shall move my parents. They are against our union and I fear they shall continue so . . .

This done, Madeleine left almost at once to spend a few days with her mother under her grandfather's roof at Ardrossan. He does not figure in person at any stage, and remains almost unknown; he was James's father, and fond of Madeleine. Her maternal grandfather, David Hamilton, died in 1843.

81

The stay was soon over and a letter went to Emile:

Yes my only love you are the only man I love or ever can love. Whatever your lott may be I shall be thine and however humble your home shall be mine. I shall share your couch no matter where—I have thought well of all this and I shall never repine though my husband is poor—no it shall be my duty to make him happy—make him forget all the sorrows of the past and look to a bright and happy future. Emile nothing can change me nothing tempt me ever to prove untrue to you—No wealth shall ever cause me to forget that I am the wife of my own my ever darling Emile. I swear to you that no man shall ever *love* me but you—Emile I dote on you I adore you with my heart and soul—I love you.

In the heat of Glasgow Emile was toiling away at Huggins and Company, spending much time with his friends, though he no longer saw much of August de Mean, now married. It seemed that pretty little Madame de Mean for some reason did not like Emile. He was quietly dropped, at least from being officially welcomed in the home of the newly married pair.

This did not worry him. He was busily engaged in enjoying the company of Dr. Francis Sievwright and family, who lived in a big house at the west end of St. Vincent Street. Emile passed several pleasant evenings there which were returned by hospitality at his lodgings; formal calling cards of Mrs. and Miss Sievwright were later found in his belongings.

He mentioned them to Madeleine: "I can assure you it will be many days before I meet such nice people as the Seaverights (*sic*) especially the daughter. I longed so much to have introduced you to her to see the perfect Lady in her and such an accomplished young person." Of Rose Sievwright's charms other correspondents have testified. Emile was just the same exercising poor tact in praising the girl to his beloved; Madeleine took it in good part and asked after the charmer with courtesy in more than one letter.

From Helensburgh, where she posted it, she sent a long discussion about money matters, bravely accepting Emile's

paltry wage as enough for them both, and with slight pathos
trying to show him how she slummed at Rowaleyn to qualify
herself for a future of poverty:

> Your income would be quite enough for me dont for one
> moment fancy I want you to better your income for me—no
> dearest I am quite content with the sum you named. When I
> first loved you I knew you were poor—I felt then I would be
> content with your *lot* however humble it might be—Yes your
> home in whatever place or whatever kind would suit me.
> If you only saw me now I am all alone in my little bedroom
> you would never mention your home as being humble. I have
> a small room on the ground floor—very small so dont fancy
> I could not put up in small rooms and with humble fare . . .
> and after our marriage we shall then laugh at our anxious
> fears. We shall make up for all the past then by loving each
> other with a sincere heart—We must trust each other. You
> shall then know all my thoughts I shall have you near me so
> I can tell you them—it is difficult to put thoughts on paper at
> least some thoughts. We shall be the envy of many—of B/
> I know. Emile never fear my friends and family casting me off.
> If they do then I shall know they are not worth having for
> friends—If they will cast me off because we are poor—why
> they will be much better away from me. If it is only for money
> your friends love you their friendship is unworthy—I will not
> love you less because you are poor—No I shall love you even
> more try to make you happy and comfortable try to make
> you forget you are poor. As you ask me I shall *burn* your last
> letter . . . I was *ill* the beginning of this week so if I should have
> the happiness to see you tuesday night I shall be quite well.
> I think I feel better this week—I cannot eat. I have not taken
> any breakfast for about two months not even a cup of tea
> nothing till I get my luncheon at 1 o/C. I dont sleep much—I
> wonder and so does M/ that my looks are not changed but I
> look as well as if I eat and slept well. I dont think I am any
> stouter but you shall judge when next you see me but I must
> go to bed as I feel cold so good night. Would to God it were
> to be by your side I would feel well and happy then—I think
> I would be wishing you to *love* me if I were with you but I dont
> suppose you would refuse me—For I know you will like to *love*

your Mimi. Adieu sweet love kind pet husband my own true Emile. I am thine forever thy wife thy devoted thy own true
MIMI L'ANGELIER—

Of the destruction of his letters so often desired by Emile, which she mentions, commentators have read into it all sorts of sinister implications. Consideration does not encourage sharing their alarm. Emile kept all her letters but perhaps did so with the knowledge they were safe in his care; Madeleine, at the mercy of a suspicious family, was more vulnerable. At any time some one could have, by chance or intent, disinterred his letters from any secret place where they were hidden.

If, which is perfectly possible, he wrote as warmly as she did, those letters in James Smith's hands would have meant an instant end of the association. Either Emile would have been driven from Glasgow, or she sent to some unknown place. Any chance of a future meeting or contact would have been destroyed completely and for good.

*　　*　　*

There have been many considerations, too, of Emile's health. That he was frequently subject to coughs and colds must have been due to his inability to grow acclimatised to Scotland ("this climate," he wrote to Elmire in 1856, "does give me so many inflammations and sore throats").

A letter written by a contemporary Jersey lady, who knew the Langeliers, mentioned Emile as sometimes subject to "slight bouts of falling sickness." There is no ancillary information other than occasional brief black-outs he endured as a youth—perhaps *petit mal*? None of the Langeliers showed any signs of epilepsy that is known, but the chance of a nervous disorder in a minor form cannot be wholly excluded in any view of Emile. Some facets of epileptic personality (classically—conceit, boastfulness, untruths, a desire to dominate, intolerance) were not wholly absent from him.

It would not do casually to condemn him for things not uncommon in perfectly healthy people. What his adult health state was cannot properly be judged for lack of good available evidence. There is one comment by Melanie: "He is not strong . . . he is delicate, of poor blood." This sounds like ordinary maternal fears, which can discover incipient illness in massive hulks of perfect male fitness.

Perhaps Emile did suffer from some disorders as a man; insomnia was one of them ("And, Anastasie, I sleep indifferently so often"). He was in a habit of using laudanum on occasions but, so careful was he of his well-being, he stuck dutifully to the "instructions on the bottle"—threaten suicide as he had in the past, he took no chance of unwittingly doing such a thing.

His other medical standby was bismuth. He had what he called a nervous stomach, by which he obviously meant dyspepsia or some form of gastric unbalance. It never showed in his youth; that it did in Glasgow is not surprising. The affair with Madeleine would have given a nervous stomach to the healthiest man alive.

She, no less than Emile, endured a good share of coughs and colds, not unusual in females in those constricted, unpleasant masses of garments of the day. Generally she had the constitution of an ox (she outlived her whole family), and a nervous system anyone could envy.

Her skin was wonderfully clear and her grey eyes always very bright ("Miss S., I recall, had such lustrous, glowing orbs" a lady who knew her wrote, wrapping a simple statement in current adjectives). She could walk for miles in any weather, play havoc with normal rest hours, and endure a complicated life requiring organisational talent of a high order, allied to constant verbal and facial dissimulation which must have demanded great mental agility.

If her letters, and her immense age at death, are any guide there was little wrong with Madeleine Smith's stamina and physical condition.

Apropos, she was five foot four in height and on the plump side only in a roundness of body; she appeared taller because of a very upright carriage and a taste for heels higher than

was the mode. It may explain why she often referred to
Emile as her "little husband." He was two inches taller than
she, but slight of build with something of *embonpoint* about
him, particularly at the waist. But, like his father, Emile was
a powerfully muscled man.

*　　　*　　　*

He continued to slip in and out of her home, and even
managed to spend time in her bedroom.

Once they were overcome by what Madeleine pleased to
call their "*lott*" when he made threats of a dramatic nature,
which brought her answer:

> Emile, if you go away and go into the French Army you know
> you will never return to Scotland—and of course I am your
> wife and I can never be the *wife* of *any other one*—So my mind
> is made up if you *go* I shall go where *no one* shall see me more
> —I shall be dead *to the World* . . .

Her promise, apparently a retreat to a nunnery rather than
into immortality, is in the best traditions of Mr. Mudie.

It was soon over. Their intimacy was renewed with the
customary doubts on her side, "we must not indulge again.
What if anything was to occur—what would they say—But
darling it is hard to resist the temptation of love."

Back again to the question of where to live after the
official ceremony, she asked, "Have you seen a lodging that
will suit us—dont mind though the rooms are small." That
he was perfectly genuine in his intentions was to be borne
out by his clerical benefactor, the Rev. Charles Miles, of St.
Jude's, who said: "He had made arrangements with his
landlady for another room, in expectation of his marriage."

The date for it was still September, when she thought she
would be "ready."

Then in an undated letter, presumed as written in July
(but, by its phrasing, possibly later), the plan had been
abandoned for no reason:

> My beloved & dearest Emile I shall begin and answer your
> dear long letter—In the first place how are you better I trust.

You know I did feel disappointed at our marriage not taking
place in Spt But as it could not why I just made up my mind
to be content and trust that it may be ere long—we shall fix
about that our next meeting which I hope wont be long—
Emile dear husband how can you express such words that you
mar my amusements and that you are a bore to me—Fie fie
dear Emile—You must not say so again you must not even
think so it is so very unkind of you. Why I would be very
unhappy if you were not near me . . . Our intimacy has not been
criminal and I am your wife before God so it has been no sin
our loving each other. No darling fond Emile I am your wife.
I shall cease to be childish and thoughtless—I shall do all I
can to please you and retain your truly dear fond love. You
know I have wished as much as you do to give you my likeness But I have not had an opportunity. I promise you you
shall have it *some* day so that promise wont be *broken* . . . It
will be a delightful bliss our union. We can not but love each
other and we shall be so kind to each other so happy. I think
when they see us P/ and M/ so happy and content they will
give in. They must in time love you. We shall be the envy of
many—My love burns for you—it increases daily—Oh to be
with you this night But I fear I would ask you to *love me* and
that would not do. No no we must not till we are married It is
hard to restrain ones passions—I do love you truly fondly.

Madeleine lived her social life to the full; she had no
other choice when her family was either entertaining visitors
to Rowaleyn, which had guest bedrooms, or was accepting
the steady stream of invitations to every sort of jollity.

Perhaps she was doing it thoughtlessly in her fondness for
gossip, but she never failed to keep Emile fully informed of
every move she made, with, maybe, a mental qualification
that she was writing at length as a dutiful wife. Out of sheer
exasperation he appears at times to have contrasted his drab
life with hers. Once more he hankered after a colourful exit
from the scene in the approved fashion, like the sorely tried
young lover has done in every age, picturing himself dying
unwanted and alone. If he made such threats the retaliatory
objections were generally by return of past:

Yes Emile you ought in those sad moments of yours to consider you have a wife—I am as much your wife as if we had been married for a year. You cannot will not leave me your wife. Oh for pitys sake dont go—I will do all you ask only remain in this country—I shall keep all my promises. I shall not be thoughtless and indifferent to you. On my soul I love you and adore you with the love of a wife—I will do anything I will do all you mention in your letters to please you only do not leave me or forsake me—I entreat of you my husband my fondly loved Emile only stay and be my guide my husband dear—You are my all my only dear love. Have confidence in me sweet pet. Trust me—Heaven is my witness I shall never prove untrue to you . . . Now Emile I shall keep all my promises I have made to you—I shall love and obey you my duty as your wife is to do so—I shall do all you want me. Trust me keep yourself easy. I know what awaits me if I do what you disapprove—of you go. That shall always be in my mind—Go never to return. The day that occurs I hope I may die. Yes I shall never look on the face of man again—You would die in Africa—Your death would be at my hands—God forbid—Trust me I love you, yes love you for yourself alone—I adore you with my heart and soul. Emile I swear to you I shall do all you wish and ask me . . .

There is no record that he answered this. Reason suggests he did the next best thing by changing his lodgings. He did not go as far as Africa but took advice from friends and went to see a landlady at 11 Franklin Place, about a mile into Glasgow from the Botanic Garden.

It was a narrow three-floored building next to a small greengrocer's shop at the eastern end of the Great Western Road, almost at the junction of St. George's Road.

Emile conducted a satisfactory interview with the prospective landlady, Mrs. Ann Jenkins, the wife of a joiner, who took a liking to her intending lodger. It was agreed he should occupy a room at the back of the first floor* and would move in at the end of July. Mrs. Jenkins, something of a

---

* Where he had the melancholy distinction of being able to see a short distance away the site where, fifty-two years later, another historic victim was to perish—Miss Marion Gilchrist, of the Oscar Slater case.

teetotaller, professed herself pleased to learn Emile was a partial abstainer but with a taste for chocolate and occasional "segars."

His association with Mrs. Clark, at the Botanic Garden, being completely friendly, he was able to arrange the move to a more convenient point without difficulty. It is to be assumed his hunger for change was temporarily satisfied.

Into the correspondence had crept a name of vital importance in the future of the lovers. First referred to in passing as "Minoch," he was at the beginning no more than one of many people, though he had acquired the correct spelling of his name when Madeleine was busily finding fault with her brothers. Village gossip must have been unusually virulent in its construction of Minnoch's visit to Rowaleyn:

> I asked Jack yesterday if he had seen you. He said Yes I saw him on Friday in a cab with a Lady and Gentleman—Said how did he look and he said he thought very cross—He has got a very fast look Jack of late—he is not improving and James is just a very bad little fellow he swears and goes on at a great rate—P/ thinks it clever. But he will be broken in when he goes to school—I think he will be a little Blackguard if he goes on at the present style . . . Minnoch was here again today —*Only* left on Saturday and back today again. He was here for four hours—He brought a fellow Weymiss with him—I think he might have a little better feeling than to come so soon knowing that every one down here has heard the report regarding myself and him—even for the people on our own place. P/ and M/ were much displeased at him—they said nothing but M/ said it was enough to make people think there was something in the report.

Emile took umbrage at the mere thought of her name being coupled with any other, even in gossip, neither did he care for the manner in which the innocent Minnoch began to feature in her letters. It could have been this which caused her to answer a wrathful protest with a hurriedly pencilled disclaimer: "What could my letter be that has made you so unhappy." She then took him to task. Emile fancied himself as an amateur artist and had sent her a drawing in good faith. It roused her quick wrath: "I did feel so cross and vexed with you—nay more I felt my temper rise—I thought you meant that picture as a caricature of myself—I felt so vexed that my husband should do such a thing to his wife."

The piqued artist rather grandly offered to take himself and his talents elsewhere, and abandon her to the omnipresent Minnoch, for "Emile forgive me—you say you 'free me' That you cannot do. There is a tie between us neither God nor man can cut asunder—I am your wife and you cannot free me No you cannot . . . Emile will you not believe I love you truly . . ."

The family proved of weaker mould than she was that week; they had "all gone to bed because the heat is so great they cannot stand it." Madeleine, scribbling industriously away, had no time for such weaknesses of the flesh. Very tactlessly she also mentioned that "Minnoch was never so pleasant as he has been this last visit."

With due ceremony Emile was completely forgiven about the offending picture. Madeleine, who at all times could ably improvise or embroider the endearments of love, did so once more but, still in a tactless mood, added a final detail which seems an invitation to trouble:

I forgive you freely from my heart for that picture never do the same thing again. I am better though I still have cold it is more my cough that annoys me. I do wish I could get rid of that cough—I often fear it is not a good cough it has been going and coming all summer but I shall take great care dear love for your sake—I hope you will get away do you not find the horror of being obliged to ask a master leave to go from home for a short time. I do wish you were your own master— Will you not try when in England to get some other situation with a larger income—I do wish you could get one out of Glasgow—You dislike Glasgow and so do I try and see what you can do while you are away . . . I did tell you at one time that I did not like William Minnoch but he was so pleasant that he quite raised himself in my estimation—I wrote to his sisters to see if they would come and visit us next week also him but they can not.

The following week she wrote again at length, having cajoled Emile out of a bad mood, when his eyes were once more on distant lands. She dilated on the "pleasure" of love, something which was to arouse the horrified wrath of the judge at the trial:

Beloved and ever dear Emile—All by myself. So I shall write to you dear husband—Your visit of last night is over—I longed for it. How fast it passed it looked but a few minutes ere you left me. You did love look cross at first but thank heaven you looked yourself ere you left Your old smile. Dear fond Emile I love you more and more—Emile I know you will not go far away from me I am your wife—You cannot leave me forever—Could you Emile—I spoke in jest of your going last night For I do not think you will go very far from me Emile your wife. Would you leave me to end my days in misery for I can never be the wife of another after our intimacy. But sweet love I do not regret that—never did and never shall. Emile were you not pleased because I would not let you *love* me last night—Your last visit you said You will not do it again till we were married. I said to myself at the time well I shall not let Emile do this again—It was a punishment to myself to be deprived of your *loving me* for it is a pleasure no one can deny that—It is but human nature—Is not everyone that *loves* of the same mind. Yes I did feel so ashamed after you left of having allowed you to see (any name you please to insert—But as you said at the time I was your wife—Emile you must consider about leaving me—I do not think you need expect to get the Australian situation . . . But to go to Australia never more to come back to your wife your Mimi—unkind of you Emile to think of such—Will nothing persuade you to remain in Huggins? Emile my husband I do not intend to make any promises as I know you wont receive them or *believe them* fearful thing but it is my own fault—But I know now what you would like me to do and what you dislike so I shall by actions try and retain your dear love . . . Your hair is so long that it makes you look—now dont be angry—not near so good looking—Are you cross at me for saying that No love you are not . . . Adieu sweet husband I am thy

WIFE THY MIMI—

To bring her to a sense of his vital part in her life (or perhaps as a dig at Minnoch), Emile's projected trip to England suddenly turned into a visit to his friends the Lanes (and their daughters) at Badgemore. He saw Madeleine before he left, still talking of possible departure to worlds beyond Henley-on-Thames. She wrote of it to him and this time brought in the heaviest guns she could think of to blow away his resolve:

Beloved husband—This time last night you were with me tonight I am all alone—Would we had not to part—Yes I long for the time when we shall be united never more to part I long for it every day—I would give the world to be with you—Yes my love to be near you to live with you. Time I hope will pass quickly when we shall be one sweet dear love—You must not leave me to go out of Europe—Emile consider your old mother if you go you will never see her more and your dear sisters and your Mimi—Can you leave me forever? Could you come and take farewell of Mimi forever. Could you break my heart by telling me this Mimi is the last time I shall see you—Could you do this Emile Emile my only love. My friends every one of them are nothing to me compared with you . . . You could not live in a far country you would die. Emile give one serious thought to it and make the resolve that you will not leave England.

With him was to go another letter, received on the day he left, with a pertly sly little dig at another lesser threat on his part. With true feminine cunning she included a comparison that was sure to work:

We are to have friends from Ireland next week among the number a very nice young fellow with a large moustache—If you wish to cut all the hair off your face why then do it but I am sure it wont improve your appearence in the least—Now be a good dear little husband of mine and excuse me writing you a longer note it is so late . . . I shall write to you at Badgemore at the end of the week about Thursday.

Indefatigably she wrote the promised letter, this time betraying a mood of despondency over an awkward bar to their secret meetings at Rowaleyn: "There is a rather sad thing about to occur to us—I am to change my room for one upstairs because they are afraid it is my bedroom that has given me a cold. So what I shall do I dont know—how can I ever see you sweet love of my soul?"

On September 29, when he was due back, a letter arrived at Franklin Place which can scarcely be called a gesture of warm welcome:

> My own ever dear Emile I did not write to you on Saturday as CH was not at home so I could not get it posted. I hope love you are home and well quite well and quite able to stand all the cold winds of winter. I am quite well quite free of cold —I dont think I can see you this week. But I think next Monday night I shall as P/ and M/ are to be in Edr but my only thought is Janet what am I to do with her? I shall have to wait till she is asleep which may be near 11 oC—But you may be sure I shall do it as soon as I can—I expect great pleasure at seeing you As a favour do not refer to what is past I shall be kind and good dear sweet love my own my best loved husband— I do love you very much—What cold weather we have had— Mr Minoch has been here since Friday he is most agreeable —I think we shall see him very often this winter he says we shall and P/ being so fond of him I am sure he shall ask him in often. I hope to hear from you soon.

As if aware how austere she must have sounded to the returned wanderer, she wrote a more affectionate word of anticipation at the end of the week: "I shall try to be out by half past 10 o/c—You said you would come by the front road up by the Pier. You will come up to our gate come in and take the narrow path on the *Left Hand* and wait there till your own Mimi comes up . . . I feel so *excited* tonight."

*   *   *

There was nothing about William Harper Minnoch which could have caused alarm.

A bachelor of thirty-four, his colouring was light and his face delicate. One letter written by one who knew him called his features "'pretty and fragile' on a Gentleman." Though short and slimly built, he was considered to be one of the best-dressed men in Glasgow.

He could well afford it, being a director of Houldsworth and Company—it was in the presence of Houldsworth and Orr, the Lord Provost, that he first made the acquaintance of James Smith.

The Minnoch house was then in East Woodside, where he lived with his sisters. But once he had met Smith, the pair achieved an instant mutual liking, and pleasure in each other's company. Rowaleyn was thrown open and Minnoch behaved with especial kindness towards Jack Smith.

It is not wholly impossible James Smith saw a probable suitor for his difficult eldest child in such an eligible man, and an antidote for her revealed passion for Emile L'Angelier. Smith did not at the time believe she was still seeing the forbidden one—if he heard so he would have thrust the fact from him if anyone had dared to voice it.

In his wisdom he must have guessed she was secretly pining for the follower paternal wrath had supposedly driven forth completely. Victorian fathers may have seemed stupid; like any fathers they were perfectly aware of the potentialities of love's rebound, and Minnoch was doubtless considered a suitable person to deal with a broken heart and repair it. William Minnoch, with every social quality, looks, background and money, could not have improved on the family requirement for a rich and suitable marriage.

He was a kindly, loyal, understanding man, whose virtues were later manifest. He was unluckily destined for a dismaying future in which the next months were to become a purgatory for him.

*   *   *

The young moon was high above the reddened autumn woods of Rowaleyn when Emile arrived for the tryst. How he felt cannot be verified but an undated letter from Mrs. Lane to a friend has survived. She mentions "the last time L'Angelier stayed with us" which was "the Autumn." It refers to the fact he "seemed overcome with melancholy for his future and about a Lady to whom he was attached." As Emile did not again stay at Badgemore, and made only one autumn visit there, the letter can be approximately dated and his mood that night at Rowaleyn presumed.

Whatever the feelings of the lovers in their reunion, its aftermath was a chilly letter, blowing hot and cold. Written the next day it suggests Minnoch was part of the evening's conversation:

Our meeting last night was peculiar. Emile you are not reasonable—I do not wonder at your not loving me as you once did —Emile I am not worthy of you. You deserve a better wife than I—I see misery before me this winter. I would to God we were not to be so near to Mr M/ You shall hear all stories and believe them. You will say I am indifferent because I am not able to see you much. I forgot to tell you last night that I shall not be able of an evening to let you in my Room is next to B/ and on the same floor as the front door—I shall never be able to spend the happy hours we did last winter—Our letters I dont see how I am to do. M/ will watch every post. I intended to speak to you of all this last night but we were so engaged otherways. I do hope you got home safe and that you have got no cold tell me love—I could not sleep all night I thought of your unhappy appearance—you shed tears love but I did not. Yes you must think me cool but it is my nature. I never did love any one till I loved you and I shall never love another—Love Emile my sweet Darling causes unhappiness in more ways than one . . . God knows dearest that I have no desire ever to be parted from you so Emile my own sweet Emile if we should ever part it will be on your side not mine. I sometimes fancy you are disappointed with me—I am not what you once thought I was I am too much of a child to please you—I am too fond of amusement to suit your fancy I am too indifferent and I do not mind what the world says not in the least—I never did—I promise to marry you knowing I would never have my fathers consent—I would be obliged to marry you in a clandestine way. I knew you were poor—All these I did not mind. I knew the world would condemn me for it but I did not mind—I trust we have days of happiness before us but God knows we have days of misery too. Emile my own my very dear husband I have suffered much on your account from my family—They have laughed at my love for you they have taunted me regarding you—I was watched all last winter I was not allowed out by myself for fear I should meet you but if I can I shall cheat them this winter. I shall avoid you at first and that may cause them to allow me out by myself. I shall write to you as often as I can but it cannot be three times a week as it has been.

Madeleine was full of contrition the next day. All was well again on her side, but if she felt the previous letter injudicious, it was needless to have sent it at all; tact was a quality she always lacked:

My own dear little Pet I hope you are well. M/ and P/ got home last night. I dont know if I should send you the note I wrote yesterday—If you dont like it burn it like a dear—I am well and I do love you very much. I hope to have a letter from you some day next week—CH. Sweet dear we are quite full of company. Saturday and Monday we are to have a large party —I shall tell you in my next letter the way I think we shall do with your Letters this winter. Adieu dear love a very fond embrace much love and kisses your own your ever dear loving little

MINI—

MADELEINE SMITH
(Impression by unknown artist and undated)

(*above*) MADELEINE SMITH'S MARRIAGE CERTIFICATE

(*Centre*)
L'ANGELIER'S DEATH
CERTIFICATE

(*Left*)
MADELEINE SMITH'S
DEATH CERTIFICATE

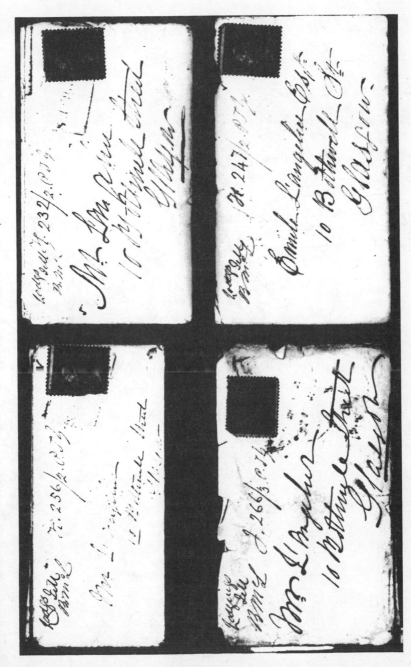

ENVELOPES ADDRESSED BY MADELEINE SMITH
(showing "disguised" handwritings)

Two letters written by
Madeleine Smith

CHAPTER EIGHT

Blythswood Square

. . . the tone and expression of the unhappy girl's letters to L'Angelier betray the corrupting influence of the guilty relationship to which she had yielded herself.
A. Duncan Smith: *Trial of Madeleine Smith.**

THE DESIRE FOR change had also smitten James Smith, who was not only tired of Rowaleyn—now too cramped for his expanding social activities—but India Street had lost its charms.

With the approach of the usual winter retreat back to Glasgow, he sought new quarters and acted on a hint from Andrew Orr, who lived at 5 Blythswood Square, which mentioned a big empty house next to his own.

Without detailed evidence it is difficult to gauge how ideas went into practice, or whose they were. It seems that Mr. Smith saw and liked the house Orr had suggested. It was suitable, but much too large.

An involved plan came about in which Smith integrated his friends and distant relatives, the Hamiltons, into the arrangements. The Hamiltons consisted of David Hamilton, a yarn merchant, and his son, William. They were to have the upper part of the house, and Smith the lower floors. There was still space to spare.

Inspiration visited either Smith or the Hamiltons, or perhaps it was William Minnoch. The decision was that he should share the upper premises as well. The Misses Minnoch do not enter into this; presumably they remained at East

---

* From the first edition published in 1905, preceding the expanded edition edited by F. Tennyson Jesse in 1927.

Woodside, leaving their brother to enjoy the pleasures of a
city bachelor apartment.

Matters went ahead. Alterations were needed, and were
simply contrived. The building had been divided in the past.
When it was ready the Smiths had their own front door on
Blythswood Square with, at the side, another front door
giving access to the upper floors, officially known as 115
Mains Street. There was still vacant space left, and this was
taken by a friend of Minnoch's, a Mr. E. Douglas, a fancy
wool merchant, who, with the Hamiltons, was never a part
of the Madeleine Smith story.

From Rowaleyn, as headquarters, organisation for a fresh
home progressed. Christina Haggart, that useful maid-
servant, was sent on to prepare things in town. Charlotte
M'Lean, family cook since September, remained to help
Mrs. Smith in the country house.

India Street was stripped in part for the move, though kept
open for a final week's interim stay between Rowaleyn and
Blythswood Square.

Madeleine came back on the eve of the actual move, finding
time on November 15, 1856, to pen a hurried note:

dearest Emile I have just arrived peeped 10 Bothwell Street but
you were not visible We are in great confusion so dearest excuse
haste I am yours affec Mimi—address 16 India St

Two days later they moved to 7 Blythswood Square where,
above, William Minnoch was already in residence.

*   *   *

The Smith headquarters require a description in view of
their importance in subsequent events.

The front door, up a set of eight stone steps, led into a
passage divided by a light door to exclude draughts. The first
door on the right was the drawing-room, with windows
commanding the Square and Mains Street; next to this was
the dining-room, also looking on the side street.

On the left of the main passage from the entrance was a set
of stone steps leading to the lower floor. The passage then

turned an angle, passing a length of blank wall (behind which
was the entrance and stairway belonging to the Minnoch
section). Next to a small pantry, bathroom and toilet, was
the bedroom taken by Mr. and Mrs. Smith, its single window
overlooking the lane at the back, serving the rear of all the
houses on that side of the Square. To the right was Bessie's
bedroom and that of Jack Smith, both overlooking Mains
Street.

At the bottom of the stone inner stairway was the lower
ground floor, also reached by an area stairway outside. This
floor had its own front door with a small bedroom just inside
on the left and, farther along, a bedroom shared by Christina
Haggart and Charlotte M'Lean. The window looked out on
the back area which was shut off from the lane by an enclosed
door in a high wall; the back door was alongside the servants'
bedroom.

Exactly beneath the dining-room on the lower floor was
the bedroom used by Madeleine and Janet Smith.

It was square, with a big closet on the right of the door,
and a fireplace on the left. On the far side were two barred
windows, their sills eighteen inches below the pavement of
Mains Street, where it sloped downhill from Blythswood
Square. Immediately on the left of the left-hand window was
the entrance to Minnoch's quarters.

The last room, below the drawing-room, was the kitchen
with windows opening on to the front area. The empty bedroom was to go to William Murray, a houseboy engaged to
live in and make himself generally useful.

Madeleine's bedroom was not of her own choosing
(though later she saw its advantages). She complained bitterly
about it to Emile: "I had a grand row with P/ this week. He
wants me to take a bedroom on the low flat in Blythswood
Sq and I dont want—I shall try and carry my point. I could
not see you though I had the chance dear love were I downstairs."

The family, not including Madeleine, liked the house, overlooking the enclosed greenery of the cobbled square. It was,

from Emile's point of view, only a few minutes' quick walk from Bothwell Street even if, in its final stages, the walk lay up a sudden incline. His lodgings, in Franklin Place, were about a half-mile distant.

*   *   *

The first letter from the new home went off on Monday, November 18, lacking neither affection nor tenderness, yet in little subtleties pointing to coming changes either foreseen or planned by Madeleine:

> My own sweet darling I am at home all safe and very well I do assure you it was with no small pleasure I received your note today—it is such a time since I have heard from you But we must so contrive that I shall hear from you every week— But I must see all about it first and shall let you know as soon as I can—derest love it shall be as you want—Though I think it is a great piece of self denial not to meet each other—Sweet love we must submit—I should so much like to see you—Do you not think I could sometimes see you at a window of a Sunday and know one would know of it? I would see you love and that would be enough. My own sweet darling husband I long to be your wife I shall be thine my own Emile whenever you like and as you say we shall do all our courting over again —We have had little of that. May our courting days last all our life—that would be happiness indeed it must be all honeymoon with us sweet love—You are a dear sweet good little pet—I dont like this house it is not at all to my mind.

A second letter on the Thursday amplified plans for future arrangements. The usual careless postscript mentioned Minnoch, whose promotion to an intimate diminutive must have caused Emile's jealousy to rise. Perhaps Madeleine realised the foolishness of what she had done; she never so described Minnoch again:

> I dont know when this may be posted perhaps not tomorrow— But love you must remember it is not easy for me to post letters for you—I can have no fixed day but depend on me sweet darling you shall have a letter whenever I can and if you do

not get one it wont be your Minis fault—Now love you must
not get angry with me sweet love—I do love you so much I do
so wish you were with me—how happy we should be in each
others embraces—When shall that be I wonder dear Emile—
It may be a long time yet—God only knows but hope for the
best all may end well—I feel quite ill in this horrid place
Glasgow I hate it so—I never thought the people looked so
vulgar as they do now—They are a most vulgar looking set . . .
Jack and I were at a Concert on Wednesday evening—I hope
you sweet pet are well free from all colds—Nice kind letter of
Miss Lanes she is a nice creature I am sure How is Mary—
Now about writing. I wish you to write to me and give me the
note on Tuesday evening next—You will about 8 oC come and
put the letter down into the window just drop it in I wont be
there at the time the window next to Minochs close door—
There are 2 windows together with white blinds. Dont be seen
near the house on Sunday as M/ wont be at Church and she
will watch—In your letter dear love tell me what night of the
week will be best for you to leave the letter for me—If M/ and
P/ were from home I could take you in very well at the front
door just the same way as I did in India St—and I wont let a
chance pass I wont sweet pet of my soul my only best loved
darling—Oh Emile I wish I could throw myself into your arms
and ask you to *love* me my dear husband—I blush to think I
write thus free to you but sweet love are you not my own sweet
husband—You will tell me if I am too free—You sweet dear
love would we could meet but it is better not it would be a
constant quarrel and that is not plesant—I shall do all you ask
me if I can I shall try and do all I can to please you my own
sweet love. I wish I were out of this horrid town what a place
it is—I would not like to spend my life in such a place.

Now you understand me Tuesday evening next between
7 and 8 oC Drop the note in between the bars on the Street
and I shall take it in—The window with white blind next to
Billys door—Adieu dear love a kiss Adieu.

It must have made him unhappy enough to protest. Her
next letter contained grumbles about the house larded with
much gossip, and she let fall a hint (presumably discussed
and known by her friends) about Minnoch. It is impossible

to know if this was deliberate intention. It seems too pat
for Madeleine, yet she possessed powers almost Machia-
vellian in their deftness at sowing seeds:

> Oh for your own wifes sake do not be sad it makes your Mimi
> sorry to think her husband is sad—Darling try not to get low
> spirited—I hope your colds are better. It is horrid cold weather
> I have a fire night and day in my Bed Room yet I am cold—
> I dislike winter weather . . . I saw Robert Anderson the other
> day—he was speaking of Huggins but he did not speak of you
> —I am so fond to hear any one speak of my own Beloved
> Mr L'Angelier—He fancies I am going to take Mr M—I am
> sure you wont like me in my jacket—I dont like it both P/
> and M/ do—My bonnet is fawn—B/ has a pink one and
> M/ wanted me to have pink but I knew you would think pink
> very vulgar—Dear love when I am your wife I shall require
> you to tell me what I am to wear as I have no idea of how to
> dress myself M/ and B/ do all that for me . . . Emile I shall tell
> you in confidence I dont think we shall ever live at Row again
> P/ is going to look at some property on Monday near Edr
> and if he can get a nice large place Row will be sold—But he
> wont sell it till he gets another. I have been ordered by the Dr
> since I came to town to take a fearful thing called "Peice
> Meal" such a nasty thing I am to take at Luncheon—I dont
> think I have tasted breakfast for two months. But I dont think
> I can take this Meal—I shall rather take cocoa.

Meetings were difficult to arrange, at least until the family
had settled into some sort of regular household routine.
Emile was compelled to make use of Madeleine's bedroom
window, guarded by bars (the sill of which was his letter box,
both for leaving and receiving letters).

It was none too easy on those winter nights. A street lamp
stood a few yards away, which meant there was no concealing
shadow. Passers-by might have commented on his form,
crouched down to whisper to her. There was always the
danger of someone going in or out of Minnoch's front door-
way, and people peering from any of the Smiths' five windows
above the road could have seen him.

The heart was clearly going out of Emile; everything seemed against him. Little things broke the smoothness of the lovers' association. Minnoch loomed larger all the time, innocently driving a wedge between them:

My very dearest Emile Your note of Friday pained me very much—I am sorry if you were put to any inconvenience by returning at 10 oC to see if your letter remained there—My husband do you suppose for an instant your wife your Mimi would forget that you mentioned in your previous letter that you would drop a note Friday night . . . For *the future* I shall take more notice of the time. The tone of your letter was so different from the last it has made me feel I assure you most unhappy—Emile my own dearest love I have done all I could to please you yet you are not pleased with me—Would I were dead and then I would annoy my husband no more—I wept for hours after I received your letter and this day I have been sad yes very sad—My Emile I love you and you only—I have tried to assure you no other has a place in my heart—It was Minnoch that   was at the concert with—You see I would not hide that from you. Emile he is Ps friend and I know he will have him at the house—But need you mind that when I have told you I have no regard for him—It is only you Emile that I love—you should not mind public report—You know I am your wife and that we shall shortly be united—so Emile it matters not. I promised you I should be seen as little in public with him as I could—I have avoided him at all times —But I could not on Wednesday night so sweet love be reasonable.

Soon after that she was unwell again, with Minnoch apparently acting as something of a watchdog—he was for some time after that completely unaware Emile existed, unless he had heard any chance mention by the family made either directly or by implication.

Then the marriage was on again, and even the hope of a child was being discussed. Emile, that good Jersiais, had obviously raised the matter, like a despairing attempt to make things as they once were. In this he was perfectly sincere, it may be noted, for he had always adored children,

and Mrs. Clark's small girl, at the Botanic Garden, had been
devoted to him.

Madeleine took up the matter, accepting the notion of a
child but with reservations:

> Beloved and best of husbands my love a fond embrace for
> thy letter of this evening. Oh how glad I am to get such letters
> from you the man I love and adore—My love my own darling
> Emile my husband ever dear I did not go to Row. I had a bad
> headache when I woke at 6 oc in the morning so I thought it
> best not to go in case of cold—I went out a little with Mama
> in the forenoon but I was in all the afternoon and as Jack did
> not leave till 5 oc he stayed at home with me and Mama and
> B/ went out—Beloved I was not out yesterday could not post
> your note which I enclose and today I could not post it with
> M/ darling . . . About those horrid Banns—love I wish we
> could do without them for if they go on friday why my old
> father will be there on Sunday to stop them And then sweet
> darling how could you trust two witnesses—Emile my sweet
> love I have often heard of clergymen in Glasgow marrying
> people with out banns &c—Just go to their house and ask them
> to marry us They would never refuse—If not that sweet love
> why not the JP And you say that a marriage by a J of Peace
> is binding why not do it—So as we are married we need not
> mind how dear love of my soul—I knew sweet love you would
> dislike my Jacket. I tell M/ and P/ I look a fright in it but they
> like them . . . Emile my husband my love you dear sweet love
> I would like to have a child because I know you are fond of
> children and I am sure I would love the child you dear love were
> the father off—Yes Emile I would be very sorry if we had no
> family only   I would be very jealous of a baby as I
> would not then get so much of your love—I would envy every
> loving word or look you bestowed on the child.

In another letter she touched on the longed-for meeting:
"Do you think beloved you could not see me some night
for a few moments at the door under the front door but
perhaps it would not be safe." She qualified this with a
nervous: "Some one might pass as you were coming in. We
had better not . . . " Aware of the possible disappointment

in raising his hopes, and then of dashing them, she finished the letter with a light touch: "Oh sweet Emile good night— Dream of your Mini but dont be *naughty* you sweet love."

* * *

William Minnoch could not be kept out of their minds. To Emile he was a constant threat, firing his jealousy. There was almost an open quarrel between himself and Madeleine just before Christmas at the bedroom window. It compelled her to write a long letter in justification:

My beloved my darling Do you for one moment think I could feel happy this evening knowing you were in low spirits and that I am the cause. O why was I ever born to annoy you best and dearest of men. Do you not wish oh yes full well I know you often wish you had never known me—I thought I was doing all I could to please you. But no When shall I ever be what you wish me to be. Never—Never! Emile will you never trust me she who is to be your wife. You will not believe me. You say you heard I took M/ to the Concert against his inclination—I forced him to go. I told you the right way when I wrote. But from your statement in your letter of tonight you *did not believe my word*. Emile I would not have done this to you—Every word you write or tell me I would believe. I *would not* believe every idle report—No I would *not*. I would my beloved Emile believe my husbands word before any other— But you always listen to reports about me if they are *bad*. But you will think I am cross—I am not but I feel hurted—Yes ah yes you my only love the only being I love with my soul should doubt my word and believe a strangers—I know I talked to him—I could not   still a whole evening without talking but I did not flirt. I gave up flirting some time ago—There is a difference between flirting and talking—He was not with me last night—he had a second rate looking girl with him of the name of Christie . . . Emile my beloved perhaps I am wrong to write you as I have done. Sweet love a kiss—Oh would to God we could meet . . . Yes my love I must see you I must be pressed to your heart . . . I hate our boy William. He stands out on the St every night and we are very angry with him—I give him a blow up every day. I just gave your note along with other 4 and said nothing. We have a nasty cook too. I am rather more fond of CH now she is very civil—I would trust her—But I shall always take in my own notes love that will please you . . . Emile Emile my beloved my darling I would love your child—could I help it. No sweet love I would adore it—I would be to it a fond mother—I would forget the suffering knowing it was a pledge of our *love*—Thank you for saying you would love me more if I had a child and that I need not be jealous. I would rather have a son as he would have a greater chance of being like his father . . . Oh these horrid Banns. I will go to Edinburgh for 21 days if that will do. I am so afraid of Glasgow people telling P/ and then there would be such a row. You see darling we would have a much greater chance of making up if we were off than if he found it out before we were married.

It seemed there was little hope of a real meeting until Mr. and Mrs. Smith went on a trip to Edinburgh, which was planned for early in January. But loving relations were resumed again in a profuse and detailed letter Madeleine sent just before Christmas in the same week: "I need not wish you a merry xmas, but I shall wish that we may spend the next together."

On Christmas Day, just before midnight, she wrote again of how tired she was of festivities (not at all surprising in view of an earlier letter stating "there are 50 coming"). Her small sister, Janet, had danced on Christmas Eve from seven o'clock until one in the morning, falling into a heavy swoon when she tried to get up after her night's sleep—in a thirteen-year-old child after such efforts it was not to be wondered at; even Madeleine had a headache.

It was a lonely Christmas Day for Emile. He had not been invited to any particular occasion but must have passed at least part of the day at Tom Kennedy's, of Huggins and Company; he wrote to Anastasie: "After a dull day spent supper with Tom and family" and, the next day, "I went to hear some singing." This may have been a secular event or it could have been at St. Jude's, where he was still a faithful member of the congregation. It was here Madeleine in the

past had slipped in once or twice for services, to see Emile
but not to speak to him. Doubtless this caused annoyance
to Dr. Beattie, of the United Presbyterian Church. He had
always taken care in person of Madeleine's religious education and appears to have been a forward old gentleman in
spite of his clerical garb. Of him she once wrote: "I saw Dr
Beattie this week and we had a quarrel because I gave him
my cheek to kiss. I told him if he did not kiss my cheek he
must want . . ."

For Emile there had been little news from Jersey. Melanie
Langelier was struggling along in the seed shop with the help
of her daughters. She boasted of having attended an English
party at Bernard Saunders' on the previous month to cele-
brate the Prince of Wales' birthday (this reads as though it
were merely an excuse to give a party); she had also gone
once to church on the Conception Day of the Virgin Mary—
otherwise she had nothing at all to tell him, only to express
anxious hopes for his health and comfort, and worry about
the Scotch winters which so troubled her son.

On December 28 Madeleine wrote Emile a warm letter;
the breach was healed as if it had never existed:

> my own beloved Emile You dear kind letter of Thursday
> I have read over and over again—It is loving kind and affte
> more than I expected love. Ah dear love why I am I not always
> what you would like me to be—But I cannot help my careless-
> ness. It is not want of love sweet dear one of my soul—I am so
> glad you do feel better take care love of yourself Get well my
> dear pet—Thank you sweet one for your assurance of love—
> I love you But oh sweet Emile I feel sad tonight and why I
> cannot tell—If I were with you I would be all right. But I feel
> ready to weep and sigh—A kiss fond love a tender long embrace
> —Sweet pet I know your love for me is great when I am good
> but you are cool when I am bad and then I try to drown my
> sad thoughts in be careless, When I get a cool letter from you
> my beloved I feel as if I did not care what I did or where I went.

She even found occasion to write warmly to Mary Perry,
about whom she had expressed doubts. Emile was still

visiting the spinster's home; perhaps he suggested Mary should write a letter, for it was this Madeleine answered with all her old friendliness.

*   *   *

With the coming of 1857, that eventful year, William Minnoch now appeared in almost every letter Madeleine wrote. Emile's protests had ceased. Either he had come to accept a rival's presence, or was cautiously biding his time to see what would happen—there was a strong streak of French canniness in him which, when he made use of it, served him well.

The lovers still had not met in private; the weeks had drifted by, almost as if the move to Blythswood Square had made a definite hiatus in their lives. On January 9 Madeleine said: "When we shall meet again I cannot tell," and there is almost a touch of yearning in the same letter:

How do you keep warm in bed for I have a fire and Janet and I are not a bit warm. I often wish I had you with me—Would you not sweet love put your arms around your Mini fondly embrace her and make her warm—Ah yes sweet one I know you would We would then be so warm so comfortable but when when shall that dear time come? God only knows. It may be a short time and alas it may be a long long time. I often wish I could get a peep into futurity. If I could see what would be in two or three years hence But perhaps it would be bad for us if we knew what would happen. I am writing in the Ding Room and I think you are again at my window but I shall not go downstairs as P/ would wonder why and only he and I are waiting up for Jack. I wish I could see you but no I must not even look out of the window as some one might see me—So beloved think it not unkind. If I never by any chance look at you just leave my note and go away—It is much the best way. Remember Janet is in my room.

Two days later she was in a state of anxious despair at not having heard from him: "Why did you not write to me to tonight my love my own sweet Emile." To this was added a

small bribe in the hope of a note from him on the window-
sill letter box: "A kiss two kisses if yours is a kind dear
letter."

He answered her the same day at length and filled it with
what she had wanted to read, and from it had taken new
heart:

> Many thanks for your kind dear long letter tonight. You are
> a dear kind sweet love. I ought to be kind to you for you are
> kinder to me than I deserve you darling—I am glad you are
> sound that is a great matter—I had a fear you were not and I
> often thought you would die but now I am easy on that point
> —I am very well but *ill* tonight—My love I shall contrive to
> see you some night soon for a short time. I do not know when
> they may go from home. I wish I could tell you sweet love I
> would so with pleasure but I dont see any chance as M/ is not
> well this winter.

It is unfortunate that so little of what Emile wrote is in
existence today. Much of Madeleine's correspondence contains mysterious allusions to things he said; his manner of
saying them would illuminate the dark places in the story.

The lovers managed to whisper frequently at the barred
window, she fearing Janet within the room might wake and
question, he crouched on the pavement wondering if chance
pedestrians would disturb them or some watching eye identify
him from the windows above.

On the third Sunday in January, by pure luck, he was able
to spend an hour with Madeleine at the window, unobserved
in spite of the moon's fading quarter and the gas-lamp
near by. She wrote gratefully of their good fortune and perhaps with no more than her usual fears, yet, in view of what
was to come, with a touch of fey quite unexpected, and
prophetic:

> You have just left me. Oh sweet darling at this moment my
> heart and soul burns with love for thee my husband my own
> sweet one—Emile what would I not give at this moment to be
> your fond wife. My night dress was on when you saw me.
> Would to God you had been in the same attire—We would be

happy. Emile I adore you—I love you with my heart and soul
—I do vex and annoy you but oh sweet love I do fondly truly
love you with my soul to be your wife your own sweet wife—
I never felt so restless and so unhappy as I have done for some
time past—I would do anything to keep sad thoughts from my
mind. But in whatever place some things make me feel sad.
A dark spot is in the future—What can it be. Oh God keep it
from us. Oh may we be happy dear darling pray for our happiness. I weep now Emile to think of our fate.

There appeared in letter after letter an air of strain, the
suggestion she was playing a part. She seemed to be giving
a forced pretence to love, whipping up her fondness by
doting affection. The first fire had died and nothing was
taking its place.

Emile, poor, alone, and often unwell, tagged along faith-
fully (perhaps sensing the falsity in what she wrote). Sometimes he protested, usually at a growing brevity. He seems a
pathetic figure, and, in his cheap clothes and stove-pipe hat,
a draggle-tailed cavalier stealing moments at a barred
window.

No longer was he the splendid conqueror who swept
through the gate into the woods of Rowaleyn, bringing
romance and glamour to convert their lives into a dream-
world of love. Her passion was fading and if her heart had
ever been in command, it was her head which now ruled her.

William Minnoch, whose intentions for so long must have
been obvious, proposed marriage at the end of January. She
accepted him but breathed no word of it to Emile.

The compact of tragedy sealed and signed at Rowaleyn
was becoming a distinct pattern, woven of inevitable strands
leading to a terrible conclusion.

CHAPTER NINE

Design for Tragedy

February 21—Miss Smith, 7 Blythswood Square, 6d.
worth arsenic for garden and country house.
Poisons' Registry, Murdoch Brothers, Druggists.

THE MASSIVE SPATE of letters, which have made this case
endure, moved gradually towards a close. All the passionate
words, the anxious entreaties, the language of devoted love,
had become thin and counterfeit. Madeleine Smith had contrived for herself a net from which there seemed no method
of escape.

Within days of a warm letter filled with affection, after
enjoying moments of happiness with Emile at the window,
and wishing she could be his wife there followed a cold,
bitter outpouring, a travesty of all that had gone before (but
in the meantime she had accepted Minnoch):

> I felt truly astonished to have my last letter returned to me.
> But it will be the last you shall have the opportunity of return-
> ing to me—When you are not pleased with the letters I send
> you then our correspondence shall be at an end and as there is
> a coolness on both sides our engagement had better be broken.
> This may astonish you but you have more than once returned
> me my letters and my mind was made up that I should not
> stand the same thing again—And you also annoyed me much
> on Saturday by your conduct in coming so near me. Altogether
> I think owing to coolness and indifference nothing else that we
> had better for the future consider ourselves as strangers—I
> trust you to your honour as a Gentleman that you will not
> reveal any thing that may have passed between us. I shall feel
> obliged by your bring me my letters and Likeness on Thursday
> eveng at 7 be at the Area Gate and CH will   the parcel

from you. On Friday night I shall send you all your letters
Likeness &ca—I trust you may yet be happy and get one more
worthy of you than I—On Thursday at 7 oC I am &c

M—

You may be astonished at this sudden change but for some
time back you must have noticed a coolness in my notes. My
love for you has ceased and that is why I was cool—I did once
love you truly fondly but for some time back I have lost much
of that love—There is no other reason for my conduct and I
think it but fair to let you know this. I might have gone on and
become your wife but I could not have loved you as I ought.
My conduct you will condemn but I did at one time love you
with heart and soul. It has cost me much to tell you this sleep-
less nights but it is necessary you should know. If you remain
in Glasgow or go away I hope you may succeed in all your
endeavours. I know you will never injure the character of one
you so fondly loved. No Emile I know you have honour and
are a Gentleman. What has passed you will not mention—I
know when I ask you that you will comply. Adieu—

On February 9 she followed this up with a short, almost
contemptuous note, without opening or signature, in which
she gave her orders in the same dictatorial, tactless fashion:

I attribute it to your having cold that I had no answer to my
last note—On Thursday evening you were I suppose afraid of
the night air. I fear your cold is not better—I again appoint
Thursday night first same place Street Gate 7 oc.

M.

If you can not send me or bring the parcel on Thursday please
write a note saying when you shall bring it and address it to
CH—Send it by post.

She could not have chosen more faulty tactics. Neither her
heart nor good sense were in these letters, and if she desired
to dismiss him, there were several ways of doing it instead
of in the fashion she decided—so many women, when they
break off a love affair, do so much in the way of a bad-
mannered queen sending a stray cur about its business as if
love suddenly grown cold needs boorishness to make quite
sure of it.

Emile L'Angelier retaliated, swiftly and devastatingly. He was many things but such a change of attitude he would not tolerate.

What he wrote is lost. It must have been a letter like nothing he had sent before, perhaps couched in terms as discourteous as her own and, to be sure, filled with anger and incredulity, the shocked stray cur biting back in startled savageness. Her answer was a veritable cry of fear and horror that her lover could turn on her. Even then she hid Minnoch with a lie when, it appears, Emile must have mentioned him:

Monday night—Emile I have just had your note—Emile for the love you once had for me do nothing till I see you—for Gods sake do not bring your once loved Mini to an open shame. Emile I have deceived you—I have deceived my Mother —God knows she did not boast of any thing I have said of you for she poor woman thought I had broken off with you last Winter. I deceived you by telling you she still knew of our engagement. She did not—This I now confess and as for wishing for any engagement with another I do not fancy she ever thought of it. Emile write to no one to Papa or any other —Oh do not until I see you on Wednesday night—be at the Hamiltons at 12 and I shall open my Shutter and then you will come to the Area Gate I shall see you. It would break my Mothers heart—Oh Emile be not harsh to me—I am the most guilty miserable wretch on the face of the earth—Emile do not drive me to death—When I ceased to love you believe me it was not to love another—I am free from all engagements at present —Emile for Gods sake do not send my letters to Papa It will be an open rupture. I will leave the house I will die—Emile do nothing till I see you. One word tomorrow night at my window to tell me or I shall go mad—Emile you did love me—I did fondly truly love you too—Oh dear Emile be not so harsh to me—Will you not, but I cannot ask forgiveness I am too guilty for that I have deceived—it was love for you at the time made me say Mama knew of our engagement. Tomorrow one word and on Wednesday we meet. I would not again ask you to love me for I know you could not—But oh Emile do not make me go mad. I will tell you that only myself and CH knew of my engagement to you. Mama did not know since last Winter.

Pray for me for a guilty wretch but do nothing. 10 oc Tomorrow
night one line for the love of God.
   Tuesday morning—I am ill. God knows what I have suffered
—My punishment is more than I can bear. Do nothing till I
see you for the love of heaven do nothing. I am mad I am ill—

He answered this, and from what he must have said (it is
reflected in her consequent reply), it has been the belief of
many commentators that here his intentions of blackmail
were first shown; others, more gentle-minded, have decided
Emile threatened to approach James Smith to stop the
marriage to Minnoch which, he may have well have sus-
pected, was the real secret.
   Facile judgments are easy, for between Emile or Madeleine
there is not very much to choose in apportioning the blame.
She was the child playing recklessly with fire, to be outraged
and frightened when it proved hot; he was despicable if he
threatened to take the letters to her father.
   But his reactions were those of the hurt lover, the outraged
"husband" who, on being unexpectedly smitten, sought for
a means to show his wrath. Some men, and usually the
weaklings, react unpleasantly at being cast forth from the
loved one's affections. They think not, neither do they consider the result of their words; they hit blindly, desiring only
to hurt, and not caring *how* they hurt so long as they do so.
It is not pretty but many spurned lovers fail to show the
public school spirit—it is difficult to imagine Cupid knows
very much about cricket.
   It was not, just the same, a manifestation of intended
blackmail or anything like it. The impulse was to smite, to
make threats terrifying in their implication. It was the
inevitable behaviour of the poorly formed, untutored mind
which, lacking any real weapons, threatens, again like the
child, "to tell your father if you aren't careful." How seldom
does that baffled yell of protest and its frustrated owner ever
get to the awful but unsuspecting parent.
   Madeleine's reply was hysterical, the distress of one who
has committed the offence and calls on God and men for pity

and pardon. It is a tragic letter, moving in its exhibition of dread, heart-rending in its picture of a soul with all barriers down and no abasement too low. Few things are so painful as human dignity grovelling before its own kind; when a woman does it, normal men feel ashamed:

Tuesday evng 12 oC Emile I have this night received your note. Oh it is kind of you to write to me—Emile no one can know the intense agony of mind I have suffered last night and today —Emile my fathers wrath would kill me you little know his temper. Emile for the love you once had for me do not denounce me to my P/ Emile if he should read my letters to you he will put me from him he will hate me as a guilty wretch. I loved you and wrote to you in my first ardent love—it was with my deepest love I loved you It was for your love I adored you—I put on paper what I should not—I was free because I loved you with my heart—If he or any other one saw those fond letters to you what would not be said of me—On my bended knees I write you and ask you as you hope for Mercy at the Judgment   do not inform on me do not make me a public shame. Emile my life has been one of bitter disappointment. You and only you can make the rest of my life peaceful —My own conscience will be a punishment that I shall carry to my grave. I have deceived the best of men—You may forgive me but God never will—for Gods love forgive me and betray me not—for the love you once had to me do not bring down my fathers wrath on me. It will kill my mother who is not well It will for ever cause me bitter unhappiness. I am humble before you and crave your mercy. You can give me forgiveness and you oh you only can make me happy for the rest of my life. I would not ask you to love me or ever make me your wife—I am too guilty for that—I have deceived and told you too many falsehoods for you ever to respect me—But oh will you not keep my secret from the world? Oh, will you not for Christs sake denounce me—I shall be undone I shall be ruined —Who would trust me—Shame would be my lot—despise me hate me but make me not the public scandal—forget me for ever blot out all remembrance of me—I have   you ill. I did love you and it was my souls ambition to be your wife. I asked you to tell me my faults—You did so and it made me cool towards you gradually—When you have found fault with me I have cooled it was not love for another for there is no one I love—My love has all been given to you—My heart is empty cold I am unloved—I am despised—I told you I had ceased to love you it was true—I did not love you as I did— but oh till within the time of our coming to Town I loved you fondly. I longed to be your wife. I had fixed Feby I longed for it—The time I could not leave my fathers house I grew discontented then I ceased to love you—Oh Emile this is indeed the true statement—Now you can know my state of mind— Emile I have suffered much for you. I lost much of my fathers confidence since that Sept—And my mother has never been the same to me. No she has never given me the same kind look. For the sake of my mother—her who gave me life spare me from shame—Oh Emile will you in Gods name hear my prayer —I ask God to forgive me—I have prayed that he might put it in your heart yet to spare me from shame. Never never while I live can I be happy—No no I shall always have the thought I deceived you—I am guilty—It will be punishment I shall bear till the day of my death—I am humbled thus to crave your pardon—But I care not—While I have breath I shall ever think of you as my best friend if you will only keep this between ourselves. I blush to ask you—Yet Emile will you not grant me this last favor—If you will never reveal what has passed. Oh for Gods sake for the love of heaven hear me. I grow mad —I have been ill very ill all day—I have had what has given me a false spirit—I have had to resort to what I should not have taken but my brain is on fire. I feel as if death would indeed be sweet—Denounce me not—Emile Emile think of our once happy days. Pardon me if you can—pray for me as the most wretched guilty miserable creature on earth. I could stand anything but my fathers hot displeasure—Emile you will not cause me death. If he is to get your letters I can not see him any more—And my poor mother—I will never more kiss her— it would be a shame to them all. Emile will you not spare me this—hate me despise me but do not expose me. I cannot write more—I am too ill tonight—

M.

PS—I cannot get to the back stair. I could never see the to it—I will take you within the door. The area

Gate will be open. I shall see you from my window. 12 oC—
I will wait till 1 oC.

That Emile heard the appeal and answered it cannot be
doubted, for, in some manner, relations approaching the
normal were restored for the moment.

* * *

In the second week of February Madeleine sent the house-
boy, William Murray, on a curious errand. She gave him a
note to fetch her a phial of prussic acid; she was in the
kitchen at the time, talking to the servants, and did not make
any particular attempt to conceal the transaction.

Murray went to what he claimed as "the nearest" druggist
in Sauchiehall Street (boy-like, he probably appreciated a
chance to dawdle in the open; in actual fact Turner, the
druggist in Mains Street, was the nearest). He came back
at last to say such a poison could not be obtained without
a doctor's prescription. Madeleine passed off the matter and
bothered no more about it, claiming she only needed it for
her hands.

One pamphlet writer later that year said this was probably
true, but did not seem to be aware of the poison's danger in
such a suggested use, particularly if it had been applied to
hands having any sort of cut or abrasion on them. Peter
Hunt's conclusion may be accepted as the only sensible one,
that she may have wanted the prussic acid for herself "in
case Emile sent her letters to Papa." At that stage the step
was feasible.

It arouses a feeling of suspicion that the action may have
triggered a different notion in her mind. Having thought of
poison, perhaps for herself, it is not improbable another
means of escape suddenly presented itself to her. It is to be
wondered if Madeleine followed this to another conclusion,
and saw a means of safety in the removal of Emile instead
of herself, if he persisted in his attitude. Knowing prussic
acid was unobtainable, even for her hands, she could have
recalled to mind the article she had once read in *Chamber's*

Journal about the cosmetic qualities of arsenic, and arsenic was not so difficult to obtain.

That apart, they were in a way reconciled—Emile saw her on Wednesday, February 11, at midnight, and again two days later. He dined at Mary Perry's on the same day, according to his own notes.

Madeleine wrote to him on February 14, a letter he received on the same day. It was warmer, more friendly than before (part of it is unreadable), and in it was a direct request for less harmful correspondence. The inference is that, in returning something she regretted sending, he might relent and send back everything:

> my dear Emile I have got my finger cut and can not write so dear I wish you would excuse me—I was glad to see you looking so well yesterday. I hope to see you very soon
> Write to me for next Thursday and then I shall tell you when I can see you—I want the first time we meet that you bring all my cool letters back the last four I have written and I will give you others in their place—Bring them all to me. Excuse me more just now it hurts mc to write so with fondest warmest and dearest love ever believe me yours with love & affection—
>
>   M.

This letter has always gone unnoticed in what *might* have resulted, had the house-boy's errand been successful. If Madeleine had used prussic acid for what she had ostensibly stated as her purpose, that cut finger would have absorbed prussic acid rapidly with consequent results depending on its strength.*

Then came a date which was to feature prominently in the trial.

On Thursday, February 19, Emile seems to have seen Madeleine for a few moments. Later that night he was very ill at his lodgings. He told Mrs. Jenkins of it in the morning, when she called him about eight o'clock. He had vomited, and on the way home to bed had been seized with racking

---

* One drop of the pure acid inside the eye of even a moderately large animal will kill it instantly.

stomach pains. It is difficult to explain the attack or wholly to understand it. Whether Madeleine can be blamed is debatable.

Since arsenic featured so prominently later on, it can be postulated but there is no conjunction between her name and the actual purchase of any arsenic until February 21. Emile's attack *could* have been due to arsenical poisoning. But Madeleine, if she had the intent, could hardly have been "trying out" a little poison; the supposition does not ring true. On the other hand, the symptoms of arsenical poisoning are essentially, in their initial stages, those of intense gastroenteritis (as unsuspecting doctors have found in the past). It would be assumption of a most unlikely cunning that Madeleine had already bought arsenic by means of a false name, given it to Emile on that occasion to start an attack which would be noticed. Then, with an eye on future mischance, openly purchased arsenic three days later in the knowledge that whatever she did with it, the illness Emile endured could not be brought home to her.

It might be wondered if the illness was one of those curious coincidences, that Emile did indeed suffer a severe attack akin to, but not caused by, poisoning. He had undergone a great mental shock and upset; there had been the crisis over Madeleine and a partial reconciliation—all in all a considerable emotional disturbance. He was subject to that nervous stomach of his, and events may have set off an extremely bad attack.

Such assumption is not entirely sound; it can be based only on the freakishness of human physiology, and idiosyncrasy. While the illness remains a mystery, Emile was well enough to go out between 10 and 11 that morning, and seemed reasonably well.

At this point must be put in a most important letter. It was headed "Wednesday" but has no date; the actual date of posting has always been a matter of dispute. After long study, the chronicler would concur with many other views, that it was written on Wednesday, February 25, 1857:

Dearest Sweet Emile I am so sorry to hear you are ill—I hope to God you will soon be better—take care of yourself —do not go to the office this week—just stay at home till Monday. Sweet love it will please me to hear you are well— I have not felt very well these last two days—sick & headache —Everyone is complaining—it must be something in the air. I cannot see you Friday as M/ is not away but I think Sunday P/ will be away & I might see you I think but I shall let you know—I shall not be at home on Saturday but I shall try sweet love and give you even if it should be a word—I cannot pass your windows or I would as you ask me to do it—do not come and walk about and become ill again—You did look bad Sunday night and Monday morning. I think you got sick with walking home so late—and the long want of food so the next time we meet I shall make you eat a loaf of bread before you go out—I am longing to meet again sweet love—We shall be so happy—I have a bad pen excuse this scroll and B/ is near me—I cannot write at night now—My head aches so and I am looking so bad that I cannot sit up as I used to do but I am taking some stuff to bring back the colour—I shall see you again soon—Put up with short notes for a little time—When I feel stronger you shall have long ones—Adieu my love my pet my sweet Emile. A fond dear tender love and sweet embrace. Ever with love yours

MINI—*

Seeming to support this is a mention in a notebook-diary kept by Emile for a brief time (see Appendix). Against the date of February 22 he recorded:

Saw Mimi in Drawing Room
Promised me French Bible
Taken very ill.

Then followed a note which could be taken as verification of the mysterious "Wednesday" letter:

Tues. 24 Feb. Wrote M.
Wed. 25 Feb. M wrote me.

* Under a high-powered hand lens the badly blurred postmark of this disputed letter shows FE, the contraction for February, and a 2—dim to the point of invisibility—but study of the mark with lens, and oblique as well as ordinary light, makes the date of February 25 almost a certainty. The year seems to be accepted and no other Wednesday in that month will serve.

What remains unqualified are two events. On the previous Friday, February 20, Emile noted down having passed two pleasant hours with Madeleine in the drawing-room. Presumably this was at Blythswood Square—but how it could have happened is inexplicable after her many excuses of not being able to ask him inside. It seems curious the servants kept out of the way for so long, assuming the whole family was absent, but there is Emile's word for it, noted in his private diary.

The following Sunday, when he was promised the French Bible, he spent an hour with her in the same place. Here a climax is reached.

On the previous day, as the Poisons' Registry of Murdoch Brothers, of Sauchiehall Street, shows, Madeleine openly bought sixpennyworth of arsenic, charging it to the house account. If she gave any of it to Emile, there was ample opportunity; the family and the servants must again have been absent. After the long weeks of their continual presence, such meetings within the guarded house defy explanation, except that of nocturnal visits which, in view of the layout of the house, seem reckless to the point of madness.

There remains the fact Emile had an attack that Sunday night like the previous one, and had a very bad time of it.

On firmer ground is Madeleine's ostensible return to the person she once was. She wrote a brief and affectionate letter on the 27th:

> My Dear Sweet Emile I cannot see you this week and I can fix no time to meet you—I do hope you are better—keep well and take care of yourself. I saw you at your window. I am better but have a bad cold I shall write to you sweet one in the beginning of the week—I hope we may meet soon. We go I think to Stirlingshire about the 10 of March for a fortnight—Excuse this short note Sweet love—With much fond tender love and kisses—And ever believe me to be yours with love
>
> MINI.

There were further letters, almost the last of them all, on the following Tuesday and Wednesday.

For Madeleine they were short and there is an air of strain about them:

On Friday we go to Stirling for a fortnight—I am sorry my dearest pet I cannot see you ere we go but I cannot. Will you sweet one write me for Thursday 8 oC and I shall get it before I go—which will be a comfort to me as I shall not hear from you till I come home again—I will write to you but sweet pet it may be only once a week as I have so many friends in that quarter—B/ is not going till next week M/ P/ J/ and I on Friday . . . I have not seen you all this week have you been passing—What nasty weather we have had—I shall see you very soon when I get home again and we shall be very happy wont we sweet one as much so as the last time—will we my pet—I hope you feel well—I have no news to give you—I am very well and I think the next time we meet you will think I look better than I did the last time—You wont have a letter from me this Saturday as I shall be off but I shall write at the beginning of the week . . .

Dearest Emile I have just time to give you a line I could not come to the window as B/ and M/ were there but I saw you —If you would take my advice you would go to the south of England for ten days it would do you much good. In fact sweet pet it would make you feel quite well—Do try and do this You will please me by getting well and strong again. I hope you wont go to B of Allan as P/ and M/ would say it was I brought you there and it would make me feel very unhappy. Stirling you need not go to as it is a nasty dirty little Town—Go to the Isle of Wight. I am exceedingly sorry love I cannot see you ere I go it is impossible but the first thing I do on my return will be to see you sweet love. I must stop as it is post time—So adieu with love and kisses and much love

I am with love and affection ever yours

MINI—

*　　*　　*

There can be no doubt that Madeleine was playing a part, simulating forms of loving affection but, under it, the touch of evasion can be sensed.

The idyll was over, had never recovered from its violent termination, but she was clinging to its ghost like a woman desperately marking time, perhaps hoping (or perhaps *knowing*) procrastination might provide the answer.

Unless she was aware of what was to come, it could have been the unfailing human belief that something would "turn up" just as that doubtful philosophy had been made so popular just seven years ago, when Wilkins Micawber had given warm life to this old belief which, if they had not thought of it before, many people accepted as a good standard for the future.

The romance was dead and no amount of effort would rekindle the embers on her side, but Madeleine Smith was still faced with the problem of William Minnoch . . . and Emile L'Angelier, her own "fond husband," who refused to be dismissed, and who held in his hands the complete dissolution of her hopes of marriage to her fiancé.

It was a seemingly unsolvable riddle. On her side to deal with it was a clear, forthright mind, a resolute character and a great deal of moral courage. With their aid, by marking time, she must have spent many hours in search of an answer, always assuming she had not already found it.

CHAPTER TEN

Death of a Lover

*And now Madeleine must have sensed that affairs were
rapidly approaching another climax, one from which there
was no escape.*

Geoffrey L. Butler: *Madeleine Smith.*

THE LOVE STORY, begun so short a time before, was almost
over. The colourful first meeting, crowned with hours of
ecstasy in the woods of Rowaleyn, moved on to an inevitable
conclusion destined to keep the names of the lovers memor-
able in the mind of the world for a hundred years.

No one can solve the unanswered problems, only guess, as
others have done, at underlying motives, yet, so repetitious
is the way of the human heart, many of the mysteries to some
extent explain themselves.

In a lesser way Emile prodded steadily at the mystery *he*
wanted solved, that of William Minnoch's standing in which
Madeleine carefully refused to commit herself. That Emile
asked question after question can be gathered from an
undated letter Madeleine apparently left for him on the
window-sill at Blythswood Square; its receipt has been
assumed as early in March:

> My sweet dear pet I am so sorry you should be so vexed—
> believe nothing sweet one till I tell you myself—it is a report
> I am sorry about—but it has been six months spoken of.
> There is one of the same kind about B/ Believe nothing till
> I tell you sweet one of my heart—I love you and you only—
> Mrs A only supposed, M/ never told her but we have found
> out that Mrs A is very good at making up stories. Mrs A
> asked me if it was M/ gave me the trinket you saw and I told
> her no. My sweet love I love you and only wish you were

124

better—we shall speak of our union when we meet—We shall be home about the 17 so may I see you about that time. I wish love you could manage to remain in town till we come as I know it will be a grand row with me if you are seen there— Could you sweet love not wait for my sake till we come home. You might go the 20th or so—I would be so very pleased with you if you can do this to please me my own dear beloved— I shall be very happy to meet you again and have as happy a meeting as the last. I have quarrelled with CH just now so cannot see you tonight—I shall write you next week.

Such evasive ambiguity exercised him sufficiently to inspire the roughing out of some questions requiring a direct answer. These he drafted on the end flyleaf of his diary-notebook:

> I insist to have an explicite
> answer to the questions you
> evaded
> Who gave you the
> tricket
> And is it true you are
> directly or indirectly engaged
> to Mr. M. or any one else
> but me. I must insist
> on this answer.

No longer was he prepared to be fobbed off. He wrote out, with his notes as a guide, an equivocal letter set forth in a kindly manner. He was neither asking unfair questions, nor being difficult; he sought bluntness and honest dealing. Madeleine could have found no fault with the tone of this, written on March 5, 1857:

> My dear, sweet pet Mimi—I feel indeed very vexed that the answer I recd yesterday to mine of Tuesday to you should prevent me from sending the kind letter I had ready for you. You must not blame me dear, for this, but really your cold, indifferent and reserved notes, so short, without a particle of love in them (especially after pledging your word you were to write me kindly for those letters you asked me to destroy) and the manner you *evaded* answering the questions I put to you

in my last, with the reports of what I hear fully convince me
Mimi that there is foundation in your marriage with another,
besides the way you put off our union till September without a
just reason is very suspicious. I do not think Mimi dear that
Mrs Anderson would say your mother told her things she had
not and really I could never believe that Mr Houldsworth
would be guilty of telling a *falsehood* for mere talking. No
Mimi, there is a foundation for all this. You often go to Mr
M/s house and common sense would lead any one to believe
that if you were not on the footing reports say you are you
would avoid going near any of his friends. I know he goes
with you or at least meets you in Stirlingshire. Mimi dear place
yourself in my position and tell me if I am wrong in believing
what I hear. I was happy the last time we met, yes very happy.
I was forgetting all the past but now it is again beginning.

Mimi I must insist in having an *explicite* answer to the
questions you evaded in my last. If you evade answering them
this time I must try some other means of coming to the truth.
If not received in a satisfactory manner you must not expect
I shall again write you personally or meet you when you return
home. I do not wish you to answer this at random. I shall wait
a day or so if you require it. I know you cannot write to me
from Stirlingshire as the time you have to write me a letter is
occupied in doing so to others. There was a time when you
would have found plenty of time.

Answer me this, Mimi—Who gave you the trinket you
showed me. Is it true it was Mr Minnoch. And is it true that
you are directly or indirectly engaged to Mr. Minnoch or to
any one else but me. These questions I must know.

The doctor says I must go to B. of A. I cannot travel 500
miles to the I. of W. and 500 back.* What is your object in
wishing me so very much to go south. I may not go to B. of A.
till Wednesday, if I can avoid going I shall do so for your sake.
I shall wait to hear from you. I hope dear, nothing will happen
to check the happiness we were again enjoying. May God bless
you Pet, and with many fond and tender embraces believe me
with kind love ever your affte husband

EMILE L'ANGELIER.

* References on both sides to the Isle of Wight is that the Lanes had a
cottage at St. Lawrence at the time and had pressed Emile to visit them on
more than one occasion.

For all that she did not make any answer. What she did do, with a promptness disconcerting in its implications (coincidence or not), was to visit a druggist, John Currie, on March 6, purchasing an ounce of arsenic "to kill rats."

On that occasion her old school-friend of Mrs. Gorton's, Mary Jane Buchanan, was there. She had been staying with her father's friends, the Dixons, in Woodside Terrace, and went round to see them all at Blythswood Square on the day of her return to Dumbarton, her home.

Madeleine told her that she wished to talk about her marriage, there being in existence the promise they had made to each other of being bridesmaids. But Mary Buchanan had no time to stop for long. Madeleine then proposed joining her friend on part of the return journey, which lay along Sauchiehall Street.

Passing Currie's shop Madeleine said:

"Oh, just stop a minute, I want to go into this shop; will you go with me?"

Mary Buchanan was quite willing. Madeleine made her purchase inside, after explaining why she wanted arsenic. She was quite open about it, yet made a curious remark: "Would sixpennyworth be a large quantity?" She should have known the answer since it was barely a fortnight before that she had bought such an amount from Murdoch Brothers.

On that same day she went with her family to stay at the Bridge of Allan, leaving the rats in temporary peace, those peculiar rodents which nobody worried about, except Madeleine Smith.

* * *

From Bridge of Allan she wrote Emile a casual, chatty letter. Its endearments were dutiful rather than natural, warm yet stilted, like another letter she sent him three days later, on Friday, March 13. Though she had already accepted William Minnoch (and, as he was to say, "arranged it more particularly on March 12"), what she wrote was compromising, and if she sought so anxiously the return of her letters, it is not easy to explain why she should add to their number.

> Dearest & Beloved I hope you are well. I am very well and anxious to get home to see you sweet one . . . I think we shall be home on Tuesday so I shall let you know my beloved sweet pet when we shall have a dear sweet interview when I may be pressed to your heart and kissed by you my own sweet love— A fond tender embrace, a kiss sweet love. I hope you will enjoy your visit here. You will find it dull no one here we know . . . Adieu my only love my own sweet pet. A kiss dear love. A tender embrace love and kisses. Adieu—Ever yours with love and fond kisses I am ever yours
>
> Mini—

It has been said that Madeleine deliberately wrote with such warmth to keep the unsuspecting Emile on a string until she could find a way out of the impasse. It may be so, but to bait such a sweetly tender trap in this manner argues a sure and shrewd mind, particularly in a letter of this nature written the day after confirming engagement to another.

These final arrangements were settled the previous day when Minnoch visited Madeleine at Bridge of Allan. June was set as the month of the wedding.

A few days later, March 16, Madeleine apparently decided that a confirmatory letter would not be amiss, and sent one to Minnoch at Houldsworth's in Glasgow. No fault can be found with its sentiments or its correctness, only in the cynical consideration of the new life together which either she hoped in a spirit of optimism would be possible because Emile might quietly fade away, or, a much more unpleasant conclusion, she *knew* would be possible because, by that time, Emile would be incapable of making any protests:*

---

* One strange item has never been referred to, and cannot be confirmed or vouched for, is a fragment of *gossip* in a letter by an outsider, seen by the chronicler. It mentions the details of the engagement and coming marriage would be given to the newspapers "about a fortnight after the engagement was settled." This was March 12; an exact fortnight would have been March 26; Emile was dead on March 23. This may be spite or sheer nonsense but could be remarkably coincidental.

My dearest William—It is but fair after your kindness to me that I should write you a note. The day I part from friends I always feel sad. But to part from one I love as I do you makes me feel truly sad and dull. My only consolation is that we shall meet soon. Tomorrow we shall be home—I do so wish you were here today. We might take a long walk. Our walk to Dumblane I shall ever remember with pleasure. That walk fixed a day on which we are to begin a new life a life which I hope may be of happiness and long duration to both of us— My aim through life shall be to please you and study you— Dear William I must conclude as Mama is ready to go to Stirling—I do not go with the same pleasure as I did last time —I hope you got to Town safe and found your sisters well. Accept my warmest kindest love and ever believe me to be yours with affecn

MADELEINE.

On that same day Emile L'Angelier, with a short leave from Huggins and Company, was at Portobello where he dined in their house at Brighton Beach with Mr. and Mrs. James Towers, the brother-in-law and a sister of Mary Arthur Perry. He was something of the talkative Emile at the meal, vain, concerned about his health and in his Gascon mood.

The discussion about himself could have been in natural sequence to one he instigated the previous Monday when taking tea with Mary Perry. He mentioned Madeleine, and told her: "I can't think why I was so unwell after getting the coffee and chocolate from her" and also said: "It is a perfect fascination my attachment to that girl; if she were to poison me I would forgive her."

At the Towers' he remarked on being accustomed to coffee but not to cocoa, pointing out that after taking cocoa he thought he had been poisoned, but mentioned no names in connection with it.

He went on to say he had taken coffee on one occasion and cocoa on another and, without qualifying further, explained he had been ill on both days after drinking them. In general he was cheerful enough and talked of his intention of returning to Glasgow and then going on to Bridge of Allan.

Elmire Langelier recalled a postcard from him at about this time, no more than the usual greetings usually sent off by people in visiting a new locality. Had he only written at length of his life just then, many questions might have been answered.

*   *   *

On the 13th Madeleine had written of her hope of being back on the Tuesday (March 17). She did return to Glasgow on that day, by way of Rowaleyn. On the same day, unaware of her return, Emile arrived from Edinburgh and called at his lodgings for her promised word as to their next meeting. Nothing had come in the post.

The next day, the 18th, Madeleine was again at Currie's for a further sixpennyworth of arsenic because the first lot had been so effective, she claimed. No less than eight or nine rats had been found dead, and with such success to support her demand, Mr. Currie could only supply her with more arsenic, but he was neither happy nor at ease about the transaction.

Meanwhile Emile was without news. He decided on the 19th to leave again. Mrs. Jenkins was told he would be home on the following Wednesday or Thursday, unless he got a letter he was expecting when he would return the same night. By going then he missed the letter containing arrangements for the meeting he desired.

He headed for Bridge of Allan by way of Edinburgh, calling there on Pollock, a Leith Street stationer, who acted as a postal address for him. Pollock had nothing, either, and Emile resumed his journey. He wrote to Mary Perry from Bridge of Allan an ordinary social letter. It revealed the expected letter had at last caught up with him:

> Dear Mary, I should have written to you before, but I am so lazy writing when away from my ordinary ways. I feel much better and I hope to be home the middle of the week.
>
> This is a very stupid place, very dull. I know no one and besides it is so very much colder than Edin. I saw your friends at Portobello and will tell you about them when I see you.

I should have come to see someone last night but the letter came too late so we are both disappointed. Trusting you are quite well and with kind regards to yourself and sister, Believe me yours sincerely,

P. EMILE L'ANGELIER

I shall be here till Wednesday.

While at Bridge of Allan Emile wrote to Tom Kennedy on March 20, inviting him on a visit:

Dear Tom, I was sorry to hear from Thuau that you were laid up. I hope by this time you are better. Are you well enough to come here tomorrow, there is a train at 12.30, 4.15, and 6.15. I think it would do you good. Plenty of Lodgings to be had here . . .

Madeleine was under the impression Emile was in Glasgow at Mrs. Jenkins, and was baffled by his silence, for, in her turn, wrote him a most urgent summons posted before noon on Saturday, March 21. This frantic letter was the last she ever wrote to him:

Why my beloved did you not come to me oh beloved are you ill come to me sweet one I waited and waited for—you but you came not I shall wait again tomorrow night same hour and arrangement oh come sweet love my own dear love of a sweet heart come beloved and clasp me to your heart come and we shall be happy a kiss fond love adieu with tender embraces ever believe me to be your own ever dear fond

MINI

This totally unpunctuated letter arrived at 11 Franklin Place on the day it was posted. Mrs. Jenkins handed it intact to Amadee Thuau, who was now a lodger in her house and who was so friendly with Emile they shared the dining-room for their meals together. Thuau sent off this letter with a covering one later that same Saturday.

Emile received it on Sunday when he called for his letters at the Bridge of Allan post office (in those days incoming mail could be collected at central post offices between 10 and 11 on Sunday mornings).

The letter seemed perfectly clear. Its postmark was distinct, *Glasgow, 21 Mr 1857*. She begged him to come again "tomorrow night" and that was today, Sunday. Emile arranged to return at once to Glasgow.

*   *   *

His nearest railway station was at Stirling, three miles away. The day was fine and he chose to walk the short distance, carrying his light bag and, no doubt, apologising first to Mrs. Bayne, his landlady, that he had to go so soon when he had meant to stay longer. At Stirling he caught the 3.30 train and travelled for twenty miles as far as Coatbridge.

There he got out, professing himself hungry. The train guard, a friendly fellow named Fairfoul, told him where he could get a meal, and Emile, his sober clothes topped off with a Glengarry bonnet or cap instead of his usual stovepipe hat, said he did not have to be in Glasgow before dark.

An auctioneer by the name of Thomas Ross got out of the train at the same time and seems to have linked up with Emile, who had some "roast beef and porter." Ross did not share this, but, both of them being due at Glasgow, they set off together on the ten-mile walk to their destination.

Emile smoked several times on the road, "walked well and did not seem tired," Ross was to say. At Glasgow the pair parted company in Gallowgate on the east side of the city at 7.30.

Mrs. Jenkins gave evidence regarding Emile's unexpected return. He told her a letter he received had brought him back.

He ate a late tea and gave her instructions about calling him early in the morning because he wished to return to Bridge of Allan. Borrowing her front door key to get in with that night, he left about nine, still wearing his holiday bonnet and a light overcoat.

Obviously too early for his usual time of seeing Madeleine, he did not hurry, and was seen a few minutes later at the west end of Sauchiehall Street, moving east, by James Galloway, a mason, who knew him by sight. Twenty minutes later Emile was beyond Blythswood Square and in a turning off St. Vincent Street, where he asked at a house for a friend of his, who was, however, not in.

*   *   *

After that Emile temporarily disappeared. Where he went has not been provably discovered, for between approximately 9.20 that evening and about 2.30 the next morning he was lost to sight.

It is a matter for wonder. This plump small man, in the light coat and Glengarry cap, somehow filled in those five hours on that quiet Glasgow Sunday night. In the near deserts of the streets, dim and lonely (the sun set just after six), even a strange cat would have been noticed, yet none came forward who had seen him.

He had his undoubted tryst to keep and keep it he must have done, perhaps to tap on Madeleine's bedroom window as was the arrangement. His destination seems certain, though Madeleine was later to claim she had not seen him for three weeks—this means that since early March she never spoke to him again.

This is the real mystery of the case, five important hours when no living creature could speak of Emile L'Angelier. He had the summons, and had gone so eagerly to answer it in order to solve the Minnoch puzzle and to seek a declaration of Madeleine's intentions, which so far she had refused to explain.

On those hours the trial was to turn. Emile was invisible from the moment he had sought his absent friend until the next morning when, racked with agony, he violently tugged at the door-bell of 11 Franklin Place to arouse Mrs. Jenkins and get her help.

*   *   *

It was about 11 o'clock on Monday morning, March 23, that Pierre Emile L'Angelier died. He had said, near the last, "Oh, my poor mother," as well he might. On Melanie's shoulders was to fall the burden and pain of the last tragedy in the sorry procession: Pierre, Zephirine, Achille, who had all died in their beds as Emile did . . . but not, as he, of arsenical poisoning.

CHAPTER ELEVEN

The First Doubts

The Procurators-Fiscal have instructions to examine into
sudden deaths, when peculiar.

James Hart, Joint Procurator-Fiscal, Glasgow.

WHEN THE JANGLING of the bell woke Ann Jenkins from sleep
at 2.30 on Monday morning, she was too cautious to unlatch
the front door, her husband being away at the time. She called
out to know who was there.

"It is I; open the door." The voice was Emile L'Angelier's.
She found him on the step, his hands clasped across his
stomach. "I am very bad; I am going to have another
vomiting of that bile."

He contrived to get up to his bedroom, giving out no
information. He drank a mouthful of water, then was very
sick but managed to ask if he might have some tea.

Before he had removed half his clothes he was sick again,
with the accompaniment of intense pain. By the light of the
gas, anxious Mrs. Jenkins could see the results of the attack
resembled the last one. She asked if he had taken anything
which disagreed with him.

"No, I have been taking nothing, and have been very well
since I was at the Bridge of Allan."

"You never took any medicine, sir?"

"I don't approve of medicine," Emile told her. This was
in keeping with his views on the subject.

He was chilly and wanted hot-water bottles for his feet
and stomach. These were brought to him, as well as three or
four extra blankets for the bed.

By four o'clock another attack racked him. Mrs. Jenkins
wanted to get the doctor. Emile refused, unless he was no

better by the morning. An hour later came a further spell, the most severe of all.

Mrs. Jenkins decided to seek medical help of her own accord, and went to fetch Dr. James Steven, who lived close by in Stafford Place. The sick man had to be assured that Steven was a good doctor.

Unfortunately Steven himself was unwell, and could not come. He advised the troubled woman to give twenty-five drops of laudanum in water, and to apply a mustard plaster to the patient's stomach, this prescription being for what he understood to be a bad bilious attack.

Emile baulked at the idea: "I never could take laudanum," though, in fact, he had taken it a number of times for insomnia. The mustard plaster was not a success; she could not make it stay in place. As the next best thing she gave him some hot water which, after causing further sickness, made him feel better but complaining of continual stomach pains and a sore throat.

At seven o'clock Mrs. Jenkins, presumably not having gone back to bed and having remained by her lodger, did not like the look of him. This paragon among landladies went again for Dr. Steven.

Like all physicians he had to do the thing with due ritual, refusing to go back with her but promising he would be along shortly. His reason, which came out at the trial, in going at last was because Emile was "a Frenchman" and "might not be understood"—Æsculapius the interpreter as opposed to the healer is something of a novelty.

He found Emile looking pinched and shrunk, grumbling about being cold. His voice was not weak at first but became so during Steven's half-hour stay; this was not through offering explanations. There were none.

A mustard plaster was tried, Emile saying continually that his breathing hurt and there was a pain in his forehead. Examination revealed his hands to be cold and his pulse weak.

Outside the bedroom the doctor comfortingly assured

Mrs. Jenkins the patient would get over it, but he would make a return visit between 10 and 11 o'clock. Emile was told this, remarking significantly: "I am worse than the doctor thinks." This could have been knowledge of how he felt, or of something he had told nobody. He certainly looked ill when he asked his landlady: "If it would not be putting you to too much trouble, I would like to see Miss Perry" and gave her the address. Of all his friends, including Madeleine, he asked for the one person who was really in his confidence.

Mrs. Jenkins did as she was asked, and was in and out of the sick-room many times. On the last occasion Emile begged her: "If you could please draw those curtains. Oh, if I could but get five minutes' peace I think I would be better." He must have been in great pain. The desire was soon to be answered.

He seemed to be sleeping when Dr. Steven returned, to be advised by Mrs. Jenkins: "He is only asleep; it is a pity to waken him."

The physician still wished to be sure all was well and went into the bedroom, bidding Mrs. Jenkins to pull back the curtains.

Emile L'Angelier was dead.

*   *   *

The silence of death can at times summon the living with the loudness of a clarion.

To Emile's side came one of Mrs. Jenkins' lodgers—fetched urgently by her small son—and, with him a grocer she knew named Robert Chrystal, who closed the dead man's eyes.

Mary Arthur Perry, small and anxious-looking, arrived just then. She wept the first tears for Emile, kissing his forehead several times in an excess of grief which surprised the landlady; she asked Miss Perry if "the intended" would be sorry about the tragedy, and was told not to say much about the intended, or, better still, to "leave the matter alone." Such a direct warning could have been perfectly

natural, but Miss Perry, who was no fool, may have had
something in mind on which she was not prepared to
elaborate.

William Stevenson, Emile's direct chief at Huggins and
Company, arrived next. While quite unsuspicious, he an-
nounced his wonder at his friend's unexpected return to
Glasgow. As a matter of routine he searched the dead man's
clothes, finding Madeleine's last message. Mrs. Jenkins at
once recognised it as "the letter that came on Saturday."
Stevenson read it and decided: "This explains all." He took
Emile's little diary-notebook after searching the room for
Melanie's address.

Dr. Hugh Thomson, Emile's own physician for the past
two years, was visited that morning by Stevenson in the
company of Amadee Thuau. They wanted a second opinion
on the cause of death. With Steven, Thomson did make an
external inspection of the body, without reaching any conclusions.

Miss Perry had gone before the doctors arrived, proceeding
direct to 7 Blythswood Square where Madeleine received
her and asked if she wished "to see mama," desiring to know
if anything was wrong (Mary Perry never explained how
Madeleine looked, if she was in any way discommoded—
indeed she was never asked such important questions).

What passed between Mary Perry and Mrs. Smith remains
unknown and here again the spinster was never asked about
the interview. It can be assumed words were not minced.
Mary Perry was fond of Emile, and was also a shrewd Scots-
woman; if she had any suspicions or doubts she may well
have voiced them. It can be suggested that perhaps class
overruled emotions, and that she had gone to the house not
to recriminate but to warn. Emile, for all his charm, remained
a danger and she could have spoken of it, initiating the closing
of ranks which later protected all the members of the Smith
family except Madeleine; *noblesse oblige* was not a *cliché*
but a rule of life a century ago.

August de Mean now stepped into the picture, as a friend

of Emile's and an acquaintance of the Smiths. That same night he exploded a bomb under James Smith's feet.

Blunt, clear-minded de Mean had no illusions. He told Smith frankly that he knew Emile possessed a large number of letters written by Madeleine "and it was high time to let him know about this" in case those letters fell into the hands of strangers.

In a sense they had. The next day de Mean saw Stevenson, the person asked by Ann Jenkins to look after the dead man's possessions and affairs. De Mean asked for the letters.

Stevenson was Emile's friend; this sudden interest must have fired his puzzled, instinctively distrustful mind. He at once took shelter in the fable of needing Mr. Huggins' authority to act, and he was out on business. De Mean could do nothing, compromising by asking that the letters should be kept sealed up until disposed of; he did not know there were well over two hundred of them in all.

The previous day Mr. Huggins had taken a personal action by calling on Dr. Thomson (at Stevenson's suggestion?) to seek more facts concerning the death of a highly satisfactory employee, a good worker who had been soundly introduced in the first place.

Thomson explained bluntly his inability to account for the death, admitting the symptoms were "such as might have been produced by an irritant poison." Had it been in England, he added, a coroner's inquest would have been held.

Stevenson very probably conferred with Mr. Huggins,* perhaps mentioning his bewilderment at de Mean's visit. The outcome of it was in Stevenson being authorised to visit Dr. Thomson and tell him Huggins and Company requested him to "make an inspection" of the body—that meant a post mortem. It took place the same day.

A short preliminary report was ready by the afternoon (see Appendix) when Drs. Thomson and Steven came to a

---

* On the 25th it was Mr. Huggins, in his determination to do all he could for L'Angelier, who caused to be inserted in the *North British Daily Mail* a notice of death.

decision which "justified a suspicion of death having resulted from poison."

* * *

William Stevenson, as a dutiful citizen, advised the Procurator-Fiscal (in Scotland the public prosecutor of a shire or other district) of the post mortem. He did not feel on that occasion there were any grounds for a criminal charge but there was a woman concerned somewhere in it.

Perhaps a woman, poison, love-letters, and his own uneasy thoughts caused the diligent Stevenson to brood; the next day, "I felt uncomfortable about the case. My feelings then pointed to a quarter where he [Emile] was likely to have been."

Nothing exceeds the wild-fire flash of suspicion. With Stevenson's deductions, fact after fact and coincidence after coincidence must have tallied. But in the Fiscal's office only careful routine inquiries were being made with no concrete ideas in the official mind.

That same Wednesday August de Mean saw Madeleine Smith at Blythswood Square, in the presence of her mother. He had seen James Smith and told the girl, in answer to her surprised questions about the call, that he came at her father's request. Her lack of tranquillity during the visit is not surprising.

De Mean explained about Emile's death and asked specifically, so that he would be able to speak in general with authority, if she had seen Emile on Sunday night. At her immediate, flat denial he mentioned the letter of assignation.

Madeleine claimed she wrote it on Friday evening, intending the appointment for Saturday night; he had never turned up.

The letter arranging this was posted between 9 a.m. and 12.30, if in a pillar box, or between 11.45 a.m. and 1 p.m., if at the main post office, on Saturday, March 21. Being addressed to Franklin Place, in Glagsow, it was thus deliverable between 1.30 and 3 that same afternoon. When the postal authorities affirmed these facts, they had a perfect post-marked envelope to guide them.

Yet Madeleine, always so careful with her exactly planned meetings and knowledge of posting times, meant by "tomorrow night," Saturday night. For all this, the letter was not posted until between breakfast and lunch on the same day as the meeting was supposed to take place.

The appointment in the previous letter, which Emile had not received in time because of his journey to Bridge of Allan, was for Thursday, March 19. He failed to keep that appointment. She therefore wrote to him, she claimed, on the very next day, Friday, begging him to be with her "tomorrow night"—Saturday.

Were she to have carried her intention to its logical conclusion, she wrote on *Friday evening* for him to be present at a Saturday night rendezvous. That being so, the latest time for posting such a message would have been early enough for it to have reached Franklin Place on the *day* it was written.

For all that she wrote it on Friday evening. At its widest latitude "evening" cannot be considered as before five o'clock. The last collection she could have caught with her letter was 5.45 at the chief post office (nowhere near Blythswood Square); this would have ensured delivery at Franklin Place by the last post of the same day. Had she put the letter into a pillar box, it would have been necessary for it to be written and posted in the afternoon—somewhere about three o'clock—to get delivery that *same* night.

Writing on Friday evening for a Saturday night meeting, it can be granted that people, in the process of writing, confuse time and, on a Friday evening the suggestion of tomorrow night as Saturday was valid, yet her written page bore no date or day.*

---

* Had the letter been written on Friday evening and she wished to get it date-stamped for the same day to make "tomorrow night" unmistakably clear, there were late collections at every railway station pillar box, and at the Royal Exchange, up till 9.30 that same evening for Saturday morning delivery.

August de Mean clearly had the same uncertainty in mind concerning the letter. He put the question "five or six different times, and in different ways" to be perfectly sure she had not seen Emile on Sunday night. De Mean even qualified it: "I told her my conviction at the moment was that she must have seen him on Sunday; that he had come on purpose from Bridge of Allan on a special invitation by her to see her; and I did not think it likely, admitting he had committed suicide, that he had committed suicide without knowing why she had asked him to come to Glasgow."

He warned her of the gravity of the case and the dangers of concealment, that somebody would perhaps have seen Emile near the house, and of the suspicions which could be aroused "as to the motives that could have led her to conceal the truth."

Madeleine got up from the chair where she had been sitting and said: "I swear to you, M. de Mean, that I have not seen L'Angelier" not only then, but for three weeks previously.

De Mean's sharp suppositions about that fatal letter, its contents and posting, must have sounded, above all other things, damning and an inkling of what appeared as a sudden, terrible danger.

Whatever it was, and it is trite to assume the guilty flee when no man pursues, Madeleine Smith went swiftly and secretly to Rowaleyn early Thursday morning, March 26.

*   *   *

When her absence was discovered in that already disturbed household, there was alarm and excitement. The Smiths were not unaware of the possibilities of a great scandal in which their eldest daughter could become involved.

Mrs. Smith obviously advised her husband of the position and told him, which she may well have hesitated over in the past because of his interdict, what she knew of Madeleine's undiminished passion for L'Angelier.

There was the occasion on the previous year when Madeleine was told by her mother she was better in her grave than married to Emile ("Papa is not at home, knows nothing of it").

Whatever Mrs. Smith assumed or believed, she cannot genuinely have thought her daughter was not in some way in contact with her forbidden lover. Mrs. Smith's nature was to retreat and it would have been true to her known character to take a comforting line of safety in ignoring an unpleasant fact or belief on the assumption that, by doing so, it would quietly go away and become non-existent.

Her energies could have been directed to ensuring her husband guessed nothing, for the sake of family peace—the secret service, the smoke screen, maintained by the women of a household can be of superlative quality. Many a shocked husband or anguished father, confronted by revelations within his home, has often in effect cried: How long has this been going on; how could it happen without my knowledge; why wasn't I *told*?

After de Mean's visit, at Smith's request, pretence was no longer possible. In the marital bedroom, away from listening ears, poor Mrs. Smith would have revealed her fears or guesses, put together a dozen little pointers which, with de Mean's keystone, became a terrifying pattern.

It is idle to ponder James Smith's reactions. Some disclosures are beyond a mere display of temper. He was a clever man, and a leading citizen. It can be reasonably decided his first reaction was to think out the best plan. He still had his good name to think of, would have checked over available ammunition and useful resources, *if* the matter was to become really serious.

Madeleine's flight, among other reasons, was guided to some extent by what she guessed of the conversation going on in her parents' bedroom. To flee was instinctive, and if she were guilty the action was the unfailing one of the killer who ably contrives murder as the curtain-like end of all encompassing difficulties, the solution of problems and what

had appeared as insurmountable barriers. That the consequence of sudden death meant questions instead of peace
and freedom is seldom visualised or expected. Flight at the
dismaying prospect of murder being a beginning, instead of
an end, can be purely automatic reflex.

Assumption apart, she had gone from the house. Into that
unhappy family circle on the morning of the discovery came
William Minnoch. He behaved admirably and intelligently
by suggesting Madeleine had perhaps gone to Rowaleyn,
for, with better psychology than any of them, he thought it
a likely place of refuge, considered through her eyes.

With Jack Smith (chosen by Minnoch's correct guess as
to her favourite and the person who would not badger her),
he set off in search. With Row as the possible goal, he could
have queried if she had boarded a steamer, best means of
making the journey, at the Glasgow Pier landing-stage. The
answer was certainly that she had boarded the early boat.

His only chance of catching her was by train to Greenock,
where local Clyde vessels called. The one means of making
the quickest connection was by the 11 o'clock train from
Bridge Street, where, so long ago, Madeleine had left on her
London journey to Mrs. Gorton's.

The pursuers found the girl when the steamer arrived at
Greenock. They decided to join her, and continue on to
Rowaleyn.

Generously enough William Minnoch did not press her
for reasons, but she volunteered the information it was
because her parents were so upset at what she had done.
He accepted this, suggesting explanations at some other time,
and took her home again, Jack carrying the overnight
carpet-bag she had taken on the journey.

Unmourned, with none to see him go, Emile L'Angelier
was laid to temporary rest on March 26 in the vault of the
Ramshorn (St. David's) Church.

Glasgow began to rock with rumour. Those close to
Emile would not have remained entirely discreet, with a
result of inevitable gossip. Many people must have noticed

Letter in L'Angelier's handwriting

THE SMITH HOUSE IN BLYTHSWOOD SQUARE

(Madeleine's two bedroom windows half sunk below pavement, above street door at the right, down slope)

(Photo: Annan, Glasgow)

Court Scene at the Trial

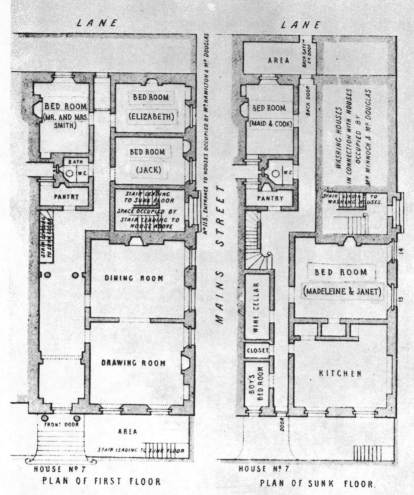

LANE   LANE

BED ROOM
(MR. AND MRS. SMITH)

BED ROOM
(ELIZABETH)

BED ROOM
(JACK)

BATH
W.C.

PANTRY

STAIR LEADING
TO SUNK FLOOR

SPACE OCCUPIED BY
STAIR LEADING TO
HOUSE ABOVE

STAIR LEADING TO SUNK FLOOR

DINING ROOM

DRAWING ROOM

FRONT DOOR

AREA

STAIR LEADING TO SUNK FLOOR

HOUSE Nº 7
PLAN OF FIRST FLOOR

No 115. ENTRANCE TO HOUSES OCCUPIED BY Mrs HAMILTON & Mr DOUGLAS

MAINS STREET

AREA

BACK GATE
OR DOOR

BACK DOOR

BED ROOM
(MAID & COOK)

W.C.

PANTRY

WASHING HOUSES
IN CONNECTION WITH HOUSES
OCCUPIED BY
Mr MINNOCH & Mr DOUGLAS

STAIR LEADING TO
WASHING HOUSES

14

WINE CELLAR

BED ROOM
(MADELEINE & JANET)

15

CLOSET

BOYS BED ROOM

DOOR

KITCHEN

HOUSE Nº 7
PLAN OF SUNK FLOOR.

BLYTHSWOOD SQUARE.

PLAN OF THE SMITH HOUSE

things—Madeleine's romance, in the sharp eyes of the world, was probably obvious, more so than she had ever guessed. With such tit-bits of scandal floating about, the story was soon all over town, talked back and forth in that constricted community.

In Jersey the news of death was to prostrate Melanie Langelier; Elmire was to recall the agony of her mother when the news of her only son's death was received.

But, unwittingly, Melanie was to bestow a morbid distinction on him. She had no money to bring him back from Scotland, and though he is still buried there, she had his name recorded on the family tombstone with his date of death, as if he really rested there.

If she could not have his dust put with the dust of his own people, his name was engraved for so long as the words would endure to show that Emile, at least in spirit, was within the comforting shelter of the island earth which bore him.

CHAPTER TWELVE

City of Rumours

It is said that the evidence at the trial will be of a very startling nature . . . it may be deemed advisable to conduct the case behind closed doors.

Morning Advertiser, May 2, 1857.

THE WEEK-END WAS a time of waiting. At Blythswood Square it cannot have been pleasant, but the Smiths, determined to maintain a united front, were at Sunday service. A lady who saw them recorded the event: "I thought she [Mrs. Smith] seemed downcast, and he [Mr. Smith] grave."

It may well be so. There is no guiding word as to Madeleine from the same source, other than of her wearing drab brown "which ill became her." Perhaps, in her uncertainty of mind, so depressing a shade must have made her seem sallow. The question of mourning, to which the Victorians were addicted, possibly exercised her mind. Such adornment, in the circumstances, would have been ostentatious, its absence equally so. Drab brown could have been a decent compromise.

Dr. Hugh Thomson had already handed to Dr. Frederick Penny, at the Andersonian University in the presence of the Fiscal's officer, a jar containing L'Angelier's stomach. Over the week-end, and for several more days, Penny worked on an analysis.

The Procurators-Fiscal, fully in action, sent a sheriff-officer, John Murray, and his assistant on Monday, March 30, with a warrant to the offices of Huggins and Company. Murray saw Stevenson and Tom Kennedy, Emile's other friend, explaining his job was to search the dead man's desk.

A mass of papers was collected. The officers then went to

Franklin Place, in Stevenson's company, where they removed
a quantity of papers and bottles.

March 31 was an important day indeed.

At about 9.30 in the morning the faithful Minnoch called
at Blythswood Square; on the previous Saturday he had
reminded Madeleine of a promise she had made when she
fled to Rowaleyn to tell him "all by and by." Of her own
accord that Monday morning, she mentioned Emile's name,
referring to the report going round that he had been poisoned.
She did not add to it other than to explain her mother could
not be seen as she was in bed, unwell—"bed seems to have
been the great resort of the elder Smiths during this period
of stress" is how Miss Tennyson Jesse puts it.

In consequence of a warrant from the Fiscal's office,
L'Angelier's body was re-examined later that morning. It
was taken from its coffin in the vault of the Ramshorn
Church in the presence of Drs. Thomson, Steven, Penny, and
Dr. Robert Corbett, of the Royal Infirmary. It was observed
the cadaver looked particularly well preserved. From it
certain parts were removed.

Then, on the same day, Madeleine received an order to
attend the office of Archibald Smith, the Sheriff-Substitute
of Lanarkshire, where he was making an examination of
various witnesses.

She was closely questioned and, after proper warning,
made a long Declaration which, in England, would be called
a statement. It was to be her only official word; at the subsequent trial she could not, of course, speak.

The Declaration, which does not contain them, was made
in answer to questions put to her. She was candid and frank,
speaking clearly and without hesitation. Her manner held
that self-contained aplomb which henceforth was particularly
to distinguish her. Though the content is long, it must be set
forth in full as her sole answer to suspicion and the later
accusations:

My name is Madeleine Smith. I am a native of Glasgow;
twenty-one years of age, and I reside with my father, James

Smith, architect, at No. 7 Blythswood Square, Glasgow. For
about the last two years I have been acquainted with P. Emile
L'Angelier, who was in the employment of W. B. Huggins &
Co., in Bothwell Street, and who lodged at 11 Franklin Place.
He recently paid his addresses to me, and I have met with him
on a variety of occasions. I learned about his death on the
afternoon of Monday the 23d March current from mamma, to
whom it had been mentioned by a lady, named Miss Perry,
a friend of M. L'Angelier. I had not seen M. L'Angelier for
about three weeks before his death, and the last time I saw him
was on a night about half-past ten o'clock. On that occasion
he tapped at my bed-room window, which is on the ground
floor and fronts Main Street. I talked to him from the window,
which is stanchioned outside, and I did not go out to him nor
did he come in to me. This occasion, which, as already said,
was about three weeks before his death, was the last time I
saw him. He was in the habit of writing notes to me, and I was
in the habit of replying to him by notes. The last note I wrote
to him was on the Friday before his death—viz., Friday the
20th March current. I now see and identify that note and the
relative envelope, and they are each marked No. 1. In consequence of that note I expected him to visit me on Saturday
night the 21st current, at my bed-room window in the same way
as formerly mentioned, but he did not come and sent no notice.
There was no tapping at my window on said Saturday night
or on the following night being Sunday. I went to bed on
Sunday night about eleven o'clock, and remained in bed till
the usual time of getting up next morning, being eight or nine
o'clock. In the course of my meetings with M. L'Angelier he
and I had arranged to get married, and we had at one time
proposed September last as the time the marriage was to take
place, and subsequently the present month of March was
spoken of. It was proposed that we should reside in furnished
lodgings; but we had not made any definite arrangement as to
time or otherwise. He was very unwell for some time, and had
gone to the Bridge of Allan for his health, and he complained
of sickness, but I have no idea what was the cause of it. I remember giving him some cocoa from my window one night
some time ago, but I cannot specify the time particularly. He
took the cup in his hand and barely tasted the contents, and

I gave him no bread to it. I was taking some cocoa myself at the time, and had prepared it myself. It was between ten and eleven p.m. when I gave it to him. I am now shown a note or letter and envelope which are marked respectively No. 2, and I recognise them as a note and envelope which I wrote to M. L'Angelier, and sent to the post. As I had attributed his sickness to want of food, I proposed, as stated in the note, to give him a loaf of bread, but I said that merely in a joke, and, in point of fact, I never gave him any bread. I have bought arsenic on various occasions. The last I bought was a sixpence-worth which I bought in Currie the apothecary's in Sauchiehall Street, and, prior to that, I bought other two quantities of arsenic, for which I paid sixpence each—one of these in Currie's, and the other in Murdoch the apothecary's shop, in Sauchiehall Street. I used it all as a cosmetic, and applied it to my face, neck, and arms, diluted with water. The arsenic I got in Currie's shop I got there on Wednesday the 18th March, and I used it all on one occasion, having put it all in the basin where I was to wash myself. I had been advised to the use of the arsenic in the way I have mentioned by a young lady, the daughter of an actress, and I had also seen the use of it recommended in the newspapers. The young lady's name was Guibilei, and I had met her at school at Clapton, near London. I did not wish any of my father's family to be aware that I was using the arsenic, and therefore never mentioned it to any of them, and I don't suppose they or any of the servants ever noticed any of it in the basin. When I bought the arsenic in Murdoch's, I am not sure whether I was asked or not what it was for, but I think I said it was for a gardener to kill rats or destroy vermin about flowers, and I only said this because I did not wish them to know that I was going to use it as a cosmetic. I don't remember whether I was asked as to the use I was going to make of the arsenic on the other two occasions, but I likely made the same statement about it as I had done in Murdoch's; and on all the three occasions, as required in the shops, I signed my name to a book in which the sales were entered. On the first occasion I was accompanied by Mary, a daughter of Dr. Buchanan of Dumbarton. For several years past Mr. Minnoch, of the firm of William Houldsworth & Co., has been coming a good deal about my father's house, and about a month ago Mr. Minnoch made a proposal of marriage to me, and I gave him my hand in token of acceptance, but no time for the marriage has yet been fixed, and my object in writing the note No. 1, before mentioned, was to have a meeting with M. L'Angelier to tell him that I was engaged in marriage to Mr. Minnoch. I am now shown two notes and an envelope bearing the Glasgow postmark of 23d January, which are respectively marked No. 3, and I recognise these as in my handwriting, and they were written and sent by me to M. L'Angelier. On the occasion that I gave M. L'Angelier the cocoa, as formerly mentioned, I think that I used it must have been known to the servants and members of my father's family, as the package containing the cocoa was lying on the mantelpiece in my room, but no one of the family used it except myself, as they did not seem to like it. The water which I used I got hot from the servants. On the night of the 18th, when I used the arsenic last, I was going to a dinner-party at Mr. Minnoch's house. I never administered, or caused to be administered, to M. L'Angelier arsenic or anything injurious. And this I declare to be truth.

(*Signed*) "MADELEINE SMITH."

The trail which began that morning in Sauchiehall Street on a draper's doorstep had reached its end, in a prison cell, the one to which Madeleine Smith was taken.

*   *   *

The integrated nature of Glasgow's merchant society revealed itself when James Smith, present at his daughter's interrogation, was at a loss as to his next action.

From one important insurance director to another, Smith in his bewilderment sought the advice of Archibald Smith, the magic wand of money and position lifting them above any mere questions of officialdom and outsider.

Archibald Smith at once recommended the solicitor acting for his own insurance company, John Wilkie, of Wilkie and Faulds, a man well versed in finding a way through the legal jungle which lay ahead.

The introduction served. James Smith had a lawyer to

look after his interests, and those of his daughter. He must
have been advised to maintain his public dignity at all costs,
for he was present in the chair a week later (April 8) at a
meeting of the Architectural Institute of Scotland, held in
their Edinburgh hall where, an observant eye noted, the
unhappy man seemed "calm, betraying nothing, alert."

While drama proceeded at a high level, the dogs of the
Fiscal's office were hard at work. In Madeleine's now deserted
bedroom they made an authorised search, departing with
Emile's photograph,* two bottles, and other items.

Newspaper comment was guarded at first, as though
editors wished to be quite certain what they were up against.
The Scotsman, on April 4, was rather dourly peeved, perhaps,
by Glasgow's grubby sins. It gave the matter a few off-hand
lines in a casual way, amplifying this later with some detail
as if it resented being dragged away from the terrible Indian
Mutiny which, since February, had caused general alarm.

Gossip did much better. Infamous rumours sped over
Glasgow, and at a time of such distinct class divisions the
have-nots enjoyed themselves considerably at the expense of
the haves. Once comment began to overflow the bank of
decent reticence, the papers picked it up—the muck-raking
American columnist of today would have found himself
perfectly at home in the lower levels of the 1857 newspaper
press.

The Fiscal's men went searching for poison sales with
steady diligence, while in his office Peter Young, the other
joint Procurator-Fiscal, took ten days to read Madeleine's
letters and set five of his clerks to work for several more days,
copying most of them in readable longhand.

The arrest had been made largely on the strength of the
correspondence, and though Dr. Penny was still at his
researches, he had obviously let prior word reach the Fiscal's
office, the quest for poison being directly made for arsenic.

* Perhaps he had endured for her sake as she had endured for his—in
November, 1856, she was in Young's, the photographer, on a five-hour stay,
most of it clamped and fastened to a chair while her daguerreotype likeness
was taken, "I was as marble."

Emile's name was sought as a possible purchaser of the poison, quite apart from Madeleine, who had already stated what she had bought.

The statutory registers were examined by John Murray in about fifty shops including, outside the city, those in Stirling, Bridge of Allan, and even on the road between Coatbridge and Glasgow. No trace was found of Emile's name; Madeleine's stated entries were verified, but not amplified by any others.

On April 6 Dr. Penny rendered his full report (see Appendix). The amount of arsenic in the dead man's stomach reached the prodigious total of 82 grains, near one-fifth of an ounce. (White arsenic, as concerns this case, is the term commonly applied to the arsenious oxide or acid, a white powder.)

*　　　*　　　*

Madeleine's legal advisers took advantage of her right as an accused person in the privilege known as "running her letters" immediately after her apprehension. This meant the public prosecutor was compelled to bring the accused to trial within a certain time, or she must be set free. Therefore the indictment had to be by May 30, and the trial by July 9 in that same year.

The Crown could have extended this delay by another process for a further forty days if desired for its own convenience. This was not done, though, in court, the Crown was to explain that its case had been prepared in a limited time. With all the written material, apart from the usual routine concerned, it must have been a mammoth task (it did, in fact, require magnifying glasses and much patient peering before Madeleine's writing could be fully deciphered; even so there were unfilled gaps).

The defence had plenty of time in which to work, or, if it proved insufficient, it could get the trial date delayed by application to the prosecutor, or to the court if he was reluctant to agree. A month later, however, the defence was

still casting round for ammunition as a letter from the
Edinburgh end of things will show:

Edinburgh, May 18, 1857
68, *Queen Street.*

Dear Sirs,
  We are agents for Miss Smith whose case is meeting so much
public discussion.
  We enclose the *North British Mail* of the 14th inst, in which
you will see a case referred to where a party at Galashiells is
said to have been cured of a disease by arsenic—Would you
be so good as to inquire into the particulars of that case—
finding out the patient and medical attendant and letting us
have their precognitions as soon as possible. Do not let it be
known that you are making inquiries in reference to Miss
Smith's case and keep your proceedings as quiet as possible.
  She is not yet indicted, and we are consequently prosecuting
our preparations for the defence a good deal at random.

Yours sincerely,
Ranken, Walker & Johnston.

Messrs Freer & Dunn,
Writers, Melrose.

  In Glasgow the firm of Moncrieff, Paterson, Forbes and
Barr were also on the defence team—Hugh Moncrieff, much
respected head of the firm, was to see his eldest son, Alexander, as one of the advocates in the trial, a notable position
for a young man who had only been called to the Scottish
Bar five years before.
  Public interest increased in proportion to the hidden progress in the case; in Scotland the accused person disappears,
as it were, until the trial. There are passionate speakers for
and against the system, some claiming it the acme of legal
procedure as opposed to the prolonged English system of
inquest, magisterial proceedings, and trial.
  But if Madeleine was neither seen nor heard, the excitement grew; Peter Hunt quotes an unnamed writer's view, a
most interesting opinion:

In point of legal evidence, there never was a case at all; and had the prisoner belonged to the lower orders, or the prejudice against her been less general, the charge would have been deserted, or never taken up. But the prevalence of sheer suspicion rendered it necessary to go on with the trial lest it should be said that favour was shown to the prisoner because of her *status* in society.

Though Madeleine was seldom out of discussion that spring, officially she knew nothing of it. In the North Prison she was conducting herself admirably, reading a great deal and seeming not too downcast at her plight. One observer's letter has mentioned her apparent indifference and stoic behaviour, soon to mark her in public, and that at times she "disturbed those in charge of her by changing moods" (an echo of a somewhat similar cry from the heart uttered in the past by Mrs. Gorton). Her visitors usually found her merry enough but frequently put out by the gloom of her parents, particularly her father.

James Smith's powerful friends acted to keep him and his family out of the case, and were able to stop any public appearance from adding to their distress. The Smiths were formidably protected, though, in fact, there was no particular necessity for them to be brought in.

The golden days moved on, while, off-stage, the law readied itself, preparing the elaborate formality of the trial at the end of June, when everything would be bared to the eyes of the expectant public.

In the woods of Rowaleyn that summer the only footsteps were ghostly ones.

CHAPTER THIRTEEN

Come to Judgment

*. . . and this you did with intent to murder the said Emile
L'Angelier . . .*

From the Indictment.

TAKEN FROM GLASGOW to the great prison which brooded
over Edinburgh, Madeleine Smith spent her last few days
before the trial in as gay a mood as ever, reading steadily,
and continually expressing her regret at having no piano to
while away the hours.

Then came the cloudy morning of June 30, 1857, when
Edinburgh was to see the opening of an event for which it
may be said a nation waited; not even Mrs. Maybrick's case
thirty two years later, or that of Lizzie Borden, aroused a
greater degree of feverish expectancy.

The High Court of Justiciary is in a cramped square, part
of the Parliament House, and facing St. Giles' Cathedral.
Grim and austere, it had seen many trials which have rocked
Scotland—Chantrelle; Laurie, the Arran murderer; Monson
(the Ardlamont case); Dr. Pritchard, whose crime a few
years later was committed close to Blythswood Square; Oscar
Slater, and Donald Merrett (Ronald Chesney).

It has recorded over the years a sorry history apart from
the glories which surrounded it, and to it, on that wet June
morning, the crowds heading for the court toiled up the
High Street to crush round the corner where the big police
office guarded the square. It seemed as if half the town was
trying to get into the court. For once the law was not asleep,
and had anticipated what was coming. An inflexible list of
rules was compiled to be obeyed, and obeyed they were.

155

At eight o'clock the main doors opened, steady groups of policemen keeping the jostlers in order, for it was a general bedlam. The seats allotted to the public were insufficient, and at least one noisy fop nearly began a riot by demanding that a doorman should admit him "for a guinea or a blow on the crown, which you please."

Within the court-room the people were cramped shoulder to shoulder. A big array of gowned Writers to Her Majesty's Signet were present with what seemed to be the entire Faculty of Advocates; twenty-seven reporters and artists; aristocrats; socialites; clergymen; civic leaders; merchants, and the ordinary public. They sweated and seethed, with a few "bold and froward" ladies to leaven the mass.

At five to ten the Lord Advocate (Moncreiff) entered, with the Solicitor-General (Maitland) and Donald Mackenzie, Advocate Depute. For the defence came the Dean of Faculty (Inglis) with his attendant advocates, George Young and Alexander Moncrieff.

The two legal stars of the case were well contrasted. The Lord Advocate, James Moncreiff, son of a baron, was a calm, grave man, a great reasoner, who went on to achieve the high office of Lord Justice-Clerk in 1869. John Inglis, the Dean of Faculty, was a minister's son, a tall, lean, eloquent pleader who ended as Lord Justice-General of Scotland and Lord President of the Court of Session; he has been likened to an Edward Clark with Marshall Hall's charm of manner.

At ten-thirty the high seats were occupied by the Lord Justice-Clerk, John Hope, a socially eminent man who was both upright and fearless, but given to a certain arrogance of manner. With him was Lord Ivory, a watchmaker's son, an amiable, impeccably honourable man of some wit, and his brother judge, Lord Handyside, another seasoned legist of marked humanity.

The first witness, Mrs. Ann Jenkins, was temporarily lost —not an unexpected thing in that crowd of people—but was soon found. Then came a hush, deep and expectant.

Ascending the trap stair of the dock Madeleine Smith, flanked by a prison matron and guardian police, came on the scene. She wore a white straw bonnet with a broad white ribbon, a black veil (raised from her face), a black silk *visite* trimmed with lace, and a fine brown silk gown with lavender gloves on her hands. She held a phial of smelling salts and used a brown shawl to cover her knees. She was fully self possessed and never for a moment lost her calm, almost detached attitude; she was the one person who never seemed to doubt the eventual outcome. A gentleman present wrote: "Her smile was ravishing, indeed lighted her somewhat plain countenance . . . I was compelled again and again to look upon her, so magnetic were her eyes. Her demeanour was both proud and unafraid . . . I observed many gentlemen near me fascinated by her to the point of open admiration."

And now she heard the elaborate indictment, pleading a clear "Not Guilty" in answer to it.

Further delay was occasioned by the non-arrival of Dr. Frederick Penny, who duly received a sharp rebuke from the Lord Justice-Clerk. Finally, with the fifteen jurors empanelled and certain legal discussions out of the way, the trial began, heralded by a sharp, accidental bang of a door near Madeleine. It caused her to jump, then smile broadly.

Scottish trials begin at once, with no opening addresses and therefore no immediate rising of tension, this growing out of whatever is contained in the statements of witnesses, from which onlookers had to piece together the trend. None of them know what is to come until it does come; the order of the prosecution's witnesses are of his own contriving.

By leading off with Ann Jenkins, the Lord Advocate was to some extent working backwards. The spectators knew Madeleine was accused of murdering Emile L'Angelier—the indictment boiled down to three charges, the first, intent to murder on February 19 or 20; the second, intent to murder on Feburary 22 or 23, and the third, murder on March 22 or 23. Nothing else had been explained, and rumours no longer counted.

Ann Jenkins, ordinary if demure in black with a white shawl, dealt with Emile's coming to her house as a lodger, his health, and identified various letters and Madeleine's picture from his room—"Is this your intended, sir?" she had asked him, to be informed, "Perhaps, some day."

With his death explained, she went under cross-examination, qualifying that "one illness was on February 22" and one "eight or ten days before this," the latter being worse than the first. She testified as to a bottle of laudanum from the dead man's room, mentioning that he had said nothing about his throat being sore. It was evidence of a general nature, specific only as to his illness and death.

The Bridge of Allan postmaster did not recognise Madeleine's famous letter of assignation, received on March 22, but agreed from its postal markings that it must have been handed over in his office. Train-guard Fairfoul, and Thomas Ross, were confirmatory witnesses to Emile's mode of travel on that last Sunday.

William Stevenson was more important, detailing Emile's association with Huggins and Company, and how he had authorised the post mortem and had discovered the letter within the clothes. The doctors told him "that an examination of his (Emile's) body was the only way of explaining his death. There was then no suspicion about it."

He vouched as to Emile's diary-notebook, which he had often seen in his desk at the office. Here the Dean held there was no evidence of the notebook being a journal at all. The Lord Advocate proposed to prove it was in Emile's handwriting.

It was, so far, conventional stuff which made the first day a muted one. There had been a brief recess at 3.30, when the judges retired and Madeleine, maintaining her calm, refused any refreshment. Stevenson's evidence was left suspended when the court finally adjourned for the day at six.

*   *   *

The second day of the trial, July 1, was bright outside but within the court the atmosphere had a flatness about it, not unlike the second night of a theatrical production. There was a hiatus in which to gather reactions into their proper place, to catch breath, and to prepare for the real difficulties to come.

Public interest had abated sufficiently to keep Parliament Square orderly if still crowded. It seemed that the man-in-the street, psychic as to trends, had guessed it was to be the day of the experts. A century ago, as today, experts were regarded as contentious people who spoke a gibberish of their own.

Court was in session at ten o'clock, Madeleine in her place as well-controlled as ever. She had varied her attire with a pair of light-blue gloves.

Maitland, the able, clear-minded Solicitor-General, took the continuation of William Stevenson's evidence.

It had scarcely begun when a mild legal squabble broke out between court and counsel regarding the letters, which Stevenson mentioned as having been handed over to the Procurators-Fiscal.

The discussion was part academic and part direct. It was thought the letters had not been treated with the care they deserved, and after examination and questions about the general handling of the letters, Stevenson was told to stand down but to be ready for a recall.

With the entrance of Dr. Hugh Thomson the hearing became scientific. The doctor covered his own part in the case, reading aloud his report on the post-mortem examination; Dr. Steven, who followed, covered almost the same ground, adding the more intimate details of his attention on Emile during the last hours.

It was with Dr. Penny—short, and with the type of head cartoonists delight to draw on a "typical" professor—that the first bombshell came. He told of his reception of the material for analysis and read out his report. He explained that he had bought ordinary arsenic from Murdoch's shop and from Currie's, after making his analysis of the body's contents.

In Murdoch's arsenic, which was 95·1 per cent arsenious acid, the remaining balance was of soot* and in Currie's it was 94·4 per cent arsenious acid, with the rest being soot and particles of indigo. It appeared that the indigo would give a blue colour in solution but was so small in quantity, it would not even discolour wine.

Penny had never heard of prussic acid being used as an external cosmetic but knew of arsenic serving as a depilatory to remove hairs from the skin when mixed with other materials such as lime (this fallacy, also displayed in the Maybrick case, still prevails, even in some expert circles. In fact the lime is depilatory, the arsenic being little more than an artistic addition).

The hearers were startled when the Dean began his cross-examination and made Penny admit to the discovery of between 82 and 83 grains of arsenic in the stomach; this is broad explanation stripped of technical detail. No determination had been made of arsenic quantities in the lungs, liver, or brain, or heart. Penny thought arsenic administered in food would largely have been ejected with vomiting, but were the poison stirred into liquid, and thus in suspension, much less would be thrown out of the body. He showed how, with dexterous manipulation, a greater part of the colouring matter in white arsenic could, with the help of water, be dispersed.

Whether or not the arsenic found in the body was the result of a single dose he could not say, and reckoned death from such poisoning could occur from half an hour of taking the dose to as long as two or three days.

Dr. Penny saw coffee or cocoa as vehicles in which arsenic could be given† but found by experiment that when 30 or 40 grains of arsenic were put into a cup of warm chocolate a

---

* By law (14 Vict c. 13, sec. 3) soot had to be mixed with all sales of arsenic of less than ten pounds.

† In *Medical Jurisprudence*, by John Glaister (1950), it is explained that 100 grains of arsenious acid mixed with two teaspoonfuls of cocoa, milk, and boiling water in a cup could not be detected by taste, appearance, or smell, but on standing the milk curdled and the arsenic sedimented.

large portion settled at the bottom of the cup, gritty particles attaching themselves noticeably to the victim's tongue and gums; in the same quantity or more, boiled with chocolate instead of being stirred, "none of it settles down." He added that though he could not separate the soot by washing from Murdoch's arsenic, much of it might be in that manner separated. With this Dr. Penny stood down, receiving a small pat from the Lord Justice-Clerk, perhaps to compensate for the criticism he got for being late; he was told that "more satisfactory, lucid or distinct evidence I never heard."

The next witness was in the nature of a Jove-like authority, a tall man still pallid from a recent illness. This was Dr. Robert Christison, for many years the leading consulting physician in Scotland and a person who excelled as an expert witness; the Crown used him on all possible occasions.

Portions of the dead man's body had been delivered to him by Dr. Penny on April 10. In the witness box he first read his report, in which he explained the finding of arsenic in the stomach, small intestine and liver. The death satisfied him as to arsenical administration, and that "being the case I should have entertained a strong suspicion in regard to his previous illnesses . . ." Dr. Christison did not know of another case in which so large a dose had been used, and thought it could have been given in chocolate or cocoa.

A long walk, he added, would have accelerated the poison's action and from half an hour to an hour would be the usual time between intake, and the manifestation of symptoms: "The very fact that poison was found on the stomach at all proves that more was given than necessary, for it is not what is left that causes the death, but what has been found on the stomach." During this testimony Madeleine showed the greatest interest in what was being said.

Amadee Thuau (curiously described by many papers as Thau or Thuot) gave his evidence through an interpreter. He outlined his knowledge of Emile, of Blythswood Square, and how the dead man had sometimes gone out at night "to his intended's house." Thuau had seen Emile on several occasions take laudanum for insomnia.

August de Mean was the next witness. Half-way through his testimony he caused a considerable stir in the public part of the court when he mentioned Madeleine's last letter to Emile, and how she had told him she carried on her correspondence before that, after becoming engaged to William Minnoch, "in order to try and get back her letters." She also told de Mean that Emile was never inside the Blythswood Square house; he had only talked to her through her barred bedroom window.

Once, "about three years" before, Emile had talked about arsenic and how much a person could take without being injured by it; Emile also told de Mean he might elope with Madeleine if her father withheld consent to the marriage. De Mean made it quite clear he thought highly of the dead man, and though he may have been of a vain and boasting disposition, he was a most exemplary character. His conclusion was that Emile was not so much jealous of Madeleine as jealous of others paying her attentions.

The court adjourned at this point, just after six, until the next day.

The morning was sunny, and revealed the great steps of St. Giles' Cathedral crowded with people as were the surrounding piazzas and the large balcony of the Union Bank; the square was solidly packed.

When the court was in session, Madeleine was observed to be restless for the first time, this becoming very marked when William Minnoch gave his evidence.

First came some formal information from a surveyor about 7 Blythswood Square, then Madeleine's Declaration was read out, to be followed by the appearance of Mary Jane Buchanan.

She was in such a state of distress that she was led to the box by her father, who remained while she gave her brief evidence. It dealt with her visit to Madeleine and the purchase of arsenic "for rats"; she mentioned that arsenic had been sought, even when the chemist advised phosphorus for the purpose. Mary Buchanan was in tears when she explained about the article read at Mrs. Gorton's concerning the taking of arsenic for health purposes.

The ordeal overcame her to such an extent that the court, desiring her to identify certain letters written by Madeleine, suggested she should retire with her father and junior counsel to make this identification elsewhere.

The same famous article on arsenic was then confirmed in the short evidence next given by Augusta Guibilei, who had been a pupil-teacher at Mrs. Gorton's.

Next came a string of witnesses to deal with various points: William Murray, the house-boy, and the druggist from whom he tried to buy prussic acid; Murdoch, and Currie, the druggists, and their assistants.

The jurors retired for lunch just after midday. Once the scarlet-robed judges had whisked out of sight, further evidence of Madeleine's strength of character was recorded by an admiring reporter: "the court becomes a miniature Babel. Everybody is discussing the evidence, while munching away at a sandwich or a biscuit. The prisoner, as usual, refuses even the slightest refreshment. Others may be thirsty amid the hot excitement, but when the female attendant offers her a glass of water, she will not have it. There she sits, refusing meat and drink, or a moment's retirement in her cell, with a smelling-bottle in her little hand, which she never used—a splendid specimen of physical power, and of such endurance as only a will of terrible strength could attain."

This steady attitude made at least one onlooker wonder if it epitomised an unflinching direction of purpose perfectly capable of committing murder: "I was sure," wrote the gentleman who had remarked on her fascination, "such was the strength capable of distilling the noxious draught which smote down the unhappy victim."

When William Minnoch arrived to give his evidence, he was so confused he went in the wrong direction and had to be guided back to the witness box. He spoke in a very low voice, clearing his throat continually and biting his lips; he never looked once at Madeleine, though she leaned forward intently to watch, as if, by will-power alone, she would make him look at her.

He told the court of the acceptance of his suit, that he was quite unaware of another man being in the picture. He electrified listeners by admitting, in innocent conjunction—"on Tuesday morning she alluded to the report that L'Angelier had been poisoned, and she remarked that she had been in the habit of buying arsenic, as she had learnt at the Clapton school that it was good for the complexion."

After this followed domiciliary evidence by Mrs. Clark about Emile's stay at the Curator's house in the Botanic Garden. Next Tom Kennedy, of Huggins and Company, added certain routine facts, and, which caused a stir in court: "He [Emile] said she had written asking for the letters. He said he would never allow her to marry another man as long as he lived. I said it was very foolish. He said he knew it was—that it was infatuation. He said, 'Tom, she will be the death of me' . . . I made the remark that the lady was not worthy of him."

The home-going public had a lot to discuss on this occasion.

* * *

On Friday morning Madeleine seemed fully composed again; she entered a court as crowded as ever, but with, for the first time, a number of women also present. They could not conceal their boredom during a discussion regarding a newspaper, *The Scottish Thistle*, which had promised to publish all the letters in the case. The Lord Justice-Clerk required to know if it meant only the letters read in court, or others as well. He demanded immediate attention by an officer of the paper to explain the matter in full.

This was followed by a further parade of minor witnesses. Next came Dr. Robert Corbett, appearing as an expert and as one of those concerned in the autopsy on L'Angelier's body. His technical evidence supported what his colleagues had already testified.

In a discussion about the dead man's jaundiced appearance, and Corbett's understanding of such matters, there was a brisk exchange with the Dean—the first signs of the strain of the trial being shown in a snappish discussion and bleak voices on both sides:

The Dean: It is your reading you referred to; I'll give you any book you name and I ask you to point out your authority:

Corbett: I know the fact.

The Dean: Not except from reading?

Corbett: No.

The Dean: Well, here it is in Dr. Taylor's book, page 62. If you find anything else there I entreat you to give it to me.

Corbett: I am not aware that it is mentioned in any other part of the article than the page to which you allude, but I would require to read it over.

The Dean: But surely, when you come here to swear as a man of skill that jaundice is a symptom of arsenical poisoning, you are prepared to give me a better answer than that. Do you know that there is a life depending on this inquiry? Pray, keep that in mind.

Corbett: Yes, I do; and I know jaundice to be a secondary symptom of arsenical poisoning from my reading.

The Dean: And is there any reading that you can condescend on except what I have pointed out to you?

Corbett: None.

There were one or two faint chuckles from the public at this interchange, which aroused the attention of the Lord Justice-Clerk. He frowned warningly.

Christina Haggart's evidence began with an explanation about marrying Duncan Mackenzie, her fiancé, whose visits Madeleine had made possible despite the views of the Smith family on followers. Christina added that she had recently left her job at Blythswood Square.

She admitted the deceptions practised on Mr. Smith so that Madeleine might have her letters, explaining how she had posted letters to Emile when out shopping. The maid's evidence did make it clear her disinterest in what was going on around her would have enabled Madeleine to receive secret visitors—this was not said, but undoubtedly implied.

Apparently, however, it was difficult to get in and out of the Blythswood Square back door because of its noise in operation. Parallel with this was the subsequent evidence given by the cook, Charlotte M'Lean, who also added an ingenuous but formidable item about the vital night of Sunday, March 22:

"I remember one night last spring remaining in the kitchen for some time with Christina Haggart. The reason she gave me for it was that some person was speaking to Miss Smith. I heard Miss Smith in the passage while I was in the kitchen. I afterwards heard her go into her bedroom, and then Christina Haggart and I went to our room. I remember Sunday, March 22, I remember Christina Haggart being unwell and keeping to her bed. I was upstairs at family worship, and left Miss Smith in the dining-room. I did not see Miss Smith that night. I heard nothing in the course of the night, and I did not hear of any person being in the house." She thought she went to bed nearer eleven than ten.

The constable on the beat at Blythswood Square had seen Emile about the house on more than one occasion, but was perfectly sure, when cross-examined by the Dean, he did not see him on the last night of all.

Little Mary Arthur Perry's evidence was delivered in a low, nervous voice. She told the story of her association with Emile and of her deep interest in him. It was a kindly, gentle recital to which listeners paid marked attention, for Mary Perry, with her spectacles sparkling beneath a large bonnet, seemed a sweet, innocuous woman led away by a soft heart and a sentimental regard for lovers.

What she did startle them with was something not dissimilar to words previously uttered by Tom Kennedy. Of Emile she explained: "He said 'It is a perfect infatuation I have for her; if she were to poison me I would forgive her.'

I said, 'You ought not to allow such thoughts to pass through your mind. What motive could she have to do you any harm?' He said, 'I don't know that; perhaps she might not be sorry to get rid of me.' All this he said in earnest. I interpreted the expression to mean to get rid of her engagement. There seemed to be some suspicions on his mind as to what Miss Smith had given him, but it was not a serious suspicion." The reference was to a cup of chocolate he had taken which had made him ill; it was on March 9 he said to Miss Perry: "I can't think why I was so unwell after getting the coffee and chocolate from her" which Miss Perry understood to refer to the separate occasions.

The day concluded with an elaborate legal discussion about the inclusion of the letters, the Dean objecting on the score of irregular and careless handling, and the manner of their recovery. There was, he contended, no proof they were the documents recovered. Nevertheless the court finally decided there was no ground to exclude the letters as evidence, and after *The Scottish Thistle* had been dealt with, in the person of its representative who explained the material he was about to publish was that so far read in evidence, the court adjourned in a gentle hum of excitement.

The letters, which for so long had been whispered about before the trial, the shocking leitmotiv of the whole case, were to be brought into the open the next day.

Saturday was to be the highlight of it all, when Victorian palates were to be titivated with matters the intending listeners thought would be quite alarming. The news was all over Edinburgh that night, and in the streets, when the almost full moon managed to peep from behind the clouds, people were seen to be gathered in knots, obviously discussing one subject.

And above the town, in the prison, Madeleine Smith waited, as calm and undisturbed as she had been all the time.

But it may be wondered how she anticipated the thought of public revelation of the intimacies of which she had written to her dead lover.

CHAPTER FOURTEEN

The Problem of Proof

That battle lay directly between two advocates.
Edgar Lustgarten: *The Woman in the Case.*

SATURDAY WAS TO be the day which surpassed them all.
The witness box had seen a stream of people testifying to
various details of fact; now the letters would be read. They
were to signal a struggle with every inch of the ground
contested.

Every assumed date, every half-obliterated postmark meant
reaction by the defence, though the reading was confined
only to the necessary. All indelicacies were avoided and
every improper sentiment left out, but first, heard almost with
impatience by the eager public, came Dr. Christison, recalled
concerning certain details.

It was in a crowded, tense room, fully packed by ten
o'clock that, startled at the eager faces about him, the doctor
entered the box. He explained that arsenic used for cosmetic
purposes would possibly cause inflammation of the eyes,
nose, and mouth; he thought there might even be dangerous
results. He went carefully into the question of taste, then
stood down.

A rustle of eagerness acknowledged the rise of the aged
Clerk of Court, holding a sheaf of papers. In a dry, unemo-
tional voice he began to read with a lack of expression, and
with steady monotony. Even he could not detract from what
he was reading. It was remarkable to hear words of passion
falling from those precise lips—he might have been giving
the stock prices or a market return for all the feeling he put
into the words.

He began with Madeleine's first letter, moving on in the breathless silence. Madeleine watched him, chin on hand and her face covered by her veil. The air was almost sultry from the sun's reflected heat. Later, violent thunder accompanied the Clerk's recital.

Only at the letter breaking off her engagement to Emile did Madeleine make any movement, an uneasy motion like a withdrawal. The audience was different; the stir was distinct. A murmur of sound, as of whispering, broke out. There was no other untoward incident when the court required certain repetitions to be made. The reading concluded with the impassioned appeal for Emile to come to her, the letter which brought him from Bridge of Allan.

A sigh, nearly a gasp, of relieved tension went up. But Madeleine had been mercifully treated by her accusers—they had made no use of the improprieties which shocked later generations of readers.

As if to revert from the colourful to the mundane, the court now began a technical discussion as to whether Emile's diary-notebook could be admitted. The judges did not care to commit themselves, deciding to render a decision on Monday. At five o'clock they rose, the whole day having been given to the letters.

The public did not hear what so shocked the Edinburgh representative of the *Durham Advertiser*, when he wrote: "I have seen accredited copies of these epistles with all the newspaper *hiatuses* filled in—copies in full integrity—and I pray God I may never see such again. Ugh!"

What had been read was meat enough for the week-end. Perhaps such expression is not absent from love letters, written by some people; in public and baldly narrated they become an offence. Somehow, in his drear recital, the Clerk of Court had managed to make them sound infinitely worse. "Before God," wrote one incensed listener, "all this freedom granted to feather-headed females is at the bottom of such sentiment. I knew not where to look as I sat there . . ."

Madeleine had recovered her poise on Monday, and heard the judges refuse to admit Emile's diary as "highly dangerous to receive as evidence a writing which may have been idle and purposeless . . ." Lord Ivory dissented with this opinion by his brothers.

Then came a Mrs. Janet Anderson, who told them of the trinket which had so absorbed Emile's attention. It was explained to her, she said, by Madeleine as being a gift from Mr. Smith, and not Minnoch. The evidence for the Crown was at an end.

The defence witnesses were a mixed bag. William Pringle Laird, and others, spoke of Emile and their knowledge of him in a series of quite colourless testimonies dealing with both the good and bad sides of his character, life, and professed suicidal tendencies.

Elizabeth Wallace, his first Glasgow landlady, told of his stay with her. His employment with Huggins and Company, and their opinion of him, was qualified by witnesses. One druggist on the road between Coatbridge and Glasgow said that somebody like Emile had come in for laudanum, and similar witnesses followed him until the impression was given that Emile had journeyed to Glasgow on that last Sunday, swigging doses of laudanum for no clear reason. Another such druggist spoke of him almost as if he was a "military gentleman"; never in his life could Emile have given such an impression.

Some more letters of Madeleine's, somewhat more to her advantage, were put in by the Dean. If anything they begged the question. He also put up Dr. Robert Paterson, a Leith physician, to speak about suicides by arsenic; he brought in, as well, Dr. Douglas Maclean, an Edinburgh physician, who offered the opinion about washing in limited quantities of arsenic as unlikely to have any ill effects. This rather pallid red herring was little more than the old game of discrediting one expert in whole or part by another. About its only advantage was in timing. Juries are apt, in dealing with technical evidence, to keep in mind the last thing they hear because it is easiest to remember.*

Some stir was created by the appearance of little Janet Smith in the box. She wore a straw hat not unlike her sister's, and, facially, resembled her to a surprising degree. Her evidence, given in a choked voice, mentioned how they had retired together in the same bed on Sunday night, March 22. Their preparations for rest had been in their customary fashion, and nothing unusual had happened. There was, the girl added, invariably a fire in the room. Madeleine was the only person in the house who took cocoa, which she usually drank in the dining-room; the packet was kept in the bed-room.

After Saturday it was really a day of anti-climax. The main matters were the character of Emile L'Angelier, the remarks he had made from time to time about suicide, and his knowledge of arsenic. For some reason the public had decided the case. The watchers were light-hearted, laughter was easily aroused, and all signs of attentive strain had gone from their faces.

It was inexplicable and illogical, but something several people remarked on when the court rose at five o'clock.

*   *   *

The Lord Advocate's speech on Tuesday took up the whole day. It was restrained and moderate, until he reached the letters, dealing with them in vital, fervent tones.

Madeleine's veil was down again and she did not move; the only sign of life she made was when, at certain strong passages, she was seen to shudder. At counsels' table the Solicitor-General stared fixedly at the floor; opposite him the Dean of Faculty compressed his lips many times at his colleague's remarks, taking occasional careful notes.

* One of the exceptions was Charles Scott King, one of the two jurors who were not for the verdict. His elaborate, if almost illegible notes, were shown to the chronicler; they certainly manage to synopsise quite admirably most of the witness evidence, but, unless the balance is lost, King appeared to tire before the final speeches were made.

Moncreiff was judicially calm in a speech that was a masterpiece of its kind, delivered without any bias but excelling in forensic expertness with no single point over-looked. It was as if he desired to sustain the disembodied honesty of justice, using immense force without for one moment relinquishing the directness of a completely fair man.

The straightforward recital of events, summarised at least twice, was impressive because it was just that. Offered as a sequence, it became arresting. Moncreiff added nothing and embellished nothing, allowing the events to stand, as it were, on their own feet.

He found Madeleine had undergone an "entire overthrow of the moral sense" and, guided by the letters, he saw in her a "depraved moral state of thought and feeling." He played on false psychology, as Edgar Lustgarten has commented, in that "it has long been a British custom—not, as yet, obsolete—to assume that sexual licence and capacity for murder are twin manifestations of one moral defect."

The Lord Advocate was scrupulous towards the living and the dead, but thought that murder was inevitable. Then, with one of the few lashes he delivered, touched on Madeleine's possession of arsenic by demanding scornfully, yet without vehemence: "She says she poured it all in a basin and washed her face in with it. Gentlemen, do you believe *that*?"

He dismissed accident or poisoning by another. On the suicide factor he asked if, after Emile received Madeleine's urgent summons, "without having gone near her house, he committed suicide?" and then: "I can conceive of no possi-bility of its being a case of suicide that does not imply that they met, and if they met, then the evidence of her guilt is overwhelming."

At the end his view was that "were there any elements of doubt or disproof," which would have justified him in retiring from his painful task, he would have rejoiced to make that retirement: "I see no outlet for the unhappy prisoner, and if you come to the same result as I have done, there is but one course open to you, and that is to return a verdict of guilty of this charge."

It was indeed strong, as strong as in any case since of a similar nature, but the fact remains the Crown could not produce any direct evidence that Madeleine and Emile were together on the crucial dates. Even so, the indirect evidence was impressive. The judges must have known, from it, that the Dean was gathering himself for a massive counter-attack; when the Lord Advocate ended at 3.30, it was suggested the court should rise until the morning.

If anything, Madeleine was faintly bored throughout, but the jury, while the address continued, had been very moved. It seemed as if they were suddenly aware of the formidable and awful responsibility about to fall on them. The trial had now become the individual concern of fifteen men. Looking at the puzzling woman in the dock was one thing; imminence to the responsibility of actually deciding whether or not she should be hanged was an entirely different matter. From being privileged spectators, they were nearing the time when they must become part of the final decision.

*   *   *

Parliament Square was packed again on Wednesday. Public attention was waiting on the defence, eager to know what it would be.

A less savoury note was observed. Betting had begun on the result and money was passed. Nineteenth-century equivalents of street-bookies were doing a roaring business. Current prices favoured the Crown, but it cannot be imagined Moncreiff would have been other than revolted, had he known of it.

The Dean of Faculty was ready the moment the court was in session. He leaned against counsels' table almost negligently, completely at ease, and delivered in four hours an almost unsurpassed speech, a gem in the forensic collection of great speeches. Edgar Lustgarten, to quote again, summarises it: "It is possible to read this speech in quiet solitude, far from the emotional pressures of a court, and to find at the end it has displaced a view already formed that Madeleine Smith should have been convicted. From this, one may dimly imagine its effect when delivered by a master at the actual trial."

To give that superb defence in disconnected extracts can serve neither its maker nor any other person. It was the reasoning of the defence and should be read, if it is to be appreciated, in its entirety.

Touching on it where necessary, it shows Inglis was out to dispel the atmosphere of the Lord Advocate's address. He changed Madeleine's position back from seeming a moral leper, then juggled Moncreiff's near-condonation of Emile's form of blackmail into a replacement of the cap on the dead man's head.

He showed how Madeleine had tried to break free near the beginning of the association in 1855, but her letters, degrading though they admittedly were, had been made so by influence: "Think you that without temptation, without evil teaching, a poor young girl falls into such depths of degradation? No."

Nevertheless, lax morals had a limit and murder was another thing, for purity was one matter and murder vastly different in every way. As to arsenic, he thought Madeleine had used it as she had claimed. He was deeply anxious that the jury should not bring in an ill-considered verdict, using as a simile the story of Eliza Fenning, a servant girl who was executed for putting arsenic in the family pudding, but who was, somewhat unhelpfully, absolved from blame when the real criminal confessed on his death-bed.

In smoothing away the two charges, and doing it wonderfully well (as he could, with those weaknesses of proof), the third and greatest charge was equally well handled, with a shrewd pointer that "we do not know what other letters he received that Sunday morning."

This was quite logical. It was impossible to say if there had been any other summons made by some unknown person (though, in fact, only Madeleine's letter was found in

Emile's clothes after his death). And, whatever else there was, people saw Emile here and saw him there, but did *not see him in Blythswood Square.*

It was almost a hammer-blow. The modern reader, well aware of the dangers of judging a man's guilt when he is found standing over a corpse, holding a smoking revolver, is versed in the impact value of a lack of direct evidence, the vital lack in the three charges.

The Dean ended "high," with tremendous force and this needs to be quoted just as he spoke:

"It may even be that the true perpetrator of this murder, if there was a murder, may be brought before the bar of this very court. I ask you to reflect for a moment what the feelings of any of us would then be. It may be our lot to sit in judgment on the guilty man. Would not our souls recoil with horror from the demand for more blood? Would not you be driven to refuse to discharge your duty in condemning the guilty because you had already doomed the innocent to die?

"I say, therefore, ponder well before you permit anything short of the clearest evidence to induce or mislead you into giving such an awful verdict as is demanded of you. Dare any man hearing me—dare any man here or elsewhere say that he has formed a clear opinion against the prisoner—will any man venture for one moment to make that assertion? And yet, if on anything short of a clear opinion you convict the prisoner, reflect how awful the consequences may be. Never did I feel so unwilling to part with a jury—never did I feel as if I had said so little as I feel now after this long address. I cannot explain it to myself, except by a strong and overwhelming conviction of what your verdict ought to be. I do feel deeply a personal interest in your verdict, for if there should be any failure of justice, I would attribute it to nothing but my own inability to conduct the defence; and I feel persuaded that, if it were so, the recollection of this day and this prisoner would haunt me as a dismal and blighting spectre to the end of life.

"May the Spirit of Truth guide you to an honest, or just, or true verdict! But no verdict will be either honest, or just, or true, unless it at once satisfies the conscientious scruples of the severest judgment, and yet leaves undisturbed and unvexed the tenderest consciences among you."

That there should be applause was inevitable. It was stopped at once.

But the Lord Justice-Clerk was not at all pleased that both counsel had expressed opinions,* one as to the guilt and one as to the innocence, of the accused: ". . . the jury were to convict only on the evidence before them, and not to be swayed by conjectures or suppositions."

The Lord Justice-Clerk began to sum up in a fair and reasoned manner, but there was little time for him to do more than open what he had to say. At six o'clock the court adjourned.

* * *

On the last morning the weather was unusually fine. It encouraged very large crowds to assemble. The police could barely control them, while those entitled to admittance had to fight their way to the main doors of the court.

Assembly was completed and the court in session by nine o'clock. Madeleine continued to betray not the slightest emotion or change of expression, but at least once, at a remark made by the Lord Justice-Clerk, she indulged in unrestrained laughter. It could have been a touch of hysteria as much as amusement, for the remark was an error rather than humour.

The summing-up went on with an air of detached solemnity, qualifying every point and clarifying any obscurities.

The Lord Justice-Clerk decided the letters displayed "ill-regulated, disorderly, distempered, licentious feeling," but, analysing what he did say, it is quite clear he did not see

---

* In *Blackwood's Magazine*, 1906, Lord Moncreiff, son of the Lord Advocate, was "astonished to find the presiding judge commencing his charge with a grave rebuke . . ." for which he found him not justified when, in particular, the Lord Advocate's speech was most restrained and moderate.

proof in the sense of the law's requirements. It could not in fact be established that Madeleine Smith had *administered* poison.

His last words require to be placed here as a temperate summary of what he had already said:

". . . and, therefore, if you cannot say we find here satisfactory evidence of this meeting, and that the poison must have been administered by her at a meeting—whatever may be your suspicion, however heavy the weight and load of suspicion is against her, and however you may have to struggle to get rid of it, you perform the best and bounden duty as a jury to separate suspicion from truth, and to proceed upon nothing that you do not find established in evidence against her.

"I am quite satisfied that whatever verdict you may give, after the attention which you have bestowed upon this case, will be the best approximation to truth at which we could arrive. But let me say also, on the other hand, as I said at the outset, that of the evidence you are the best judges, not only in point of law, but in point of fact; and you may be perfectly confident that, if you return a verdict satisfactory to yourselves against the prisoner, you need not fear any consequences from any future, or imagined, or fancied discovery, which may take place. You have done your duty under your oaths, under God, and to your country, and may feel satisfied that remorse you never can have."

At one o'clock the fifteen jurymen retired, leaving a silent and puzzled audience. It was as if those who "knew" had suddenly been stricken with doubts about the verdict.

CHAPTER FIFTEEN

Storm over Scotland

*The jury were not satisfied, and we cannot now say that
they were wrong.*

Lord Birkenhead: *Famous Trials.*

AT ONE-THIRTY THE jury-room bell sounded. A brief flurry
broke the court-room hush; some thought it was an adverse
verdict after so short a time, others, with equal logic, decided
it meant favour to the accused. The experts were inclined to
wonder if further guidance was sought. But a verdict had
been reached.

With the reassembly of the court, and the jury in their box
again, the Lord Justice-Clerk sternly warned the audience
there would be no exhibition of feeling of any sort.

The Clerk of Court slowly called over the names of the
jurors one by one, then requested their foreman to give his
verdict.

The foreman was a lean, nervous-looking man named
William Moffat, a teacher in Edinburgh High School. He
stood, a piece of paper in his hands, and tears in his eyes—
other members of the jury had openly wept. He spoke very
slowly:

"In respect of the first count in the indictment, the jury,
by a majority, find the pannel Not Guilty; in respect to the
second count, the jury find, by a majority, the charge against
the prisoner Not Proven; and in respect to the third count,
the jury find, by a majority, the charge Not Proven." In each
case the verdict was thirteen to two; in Scotland the majority
decision stood, unlike England.

The public let out an instant burst of applause and loud
clapping, which could not be stemmed. The irate Lord

Justice-Clerk's eye fell on a furiously enthusiastic young man in the gallery above, and ordered him to be taken at once into custody.

Madeleine smiled uncertainly at the verdict, her composure unbroken, but she was fighting to maintain it. The prison matron took one of her hands in congratulation, and Mr. Ranken, Madeleine's solicitor, took her other hand.

She was free but, nevertheless, the Dean of Faculty did not approach her, nor look nor make any move in her direction.*

The uproar outside was phenomenal. People shouted and danced, while on the steps of the court one young man was screaming in wild excitement, telling all who would listen he had won thirty guineas on the result. One commentator on the scene thought the enthusiasm was as much over bets won as the good fortune of the accused.

The verdict meant the jury had compromised with itself. Not Proven does not settle complete innocence or complete guilt, being exactly what it says. That the party at the receiving end is neither washed white nor left black is obvious, but left with a permanently smeared character—the cynical have always said the verdict means in effect: "Not Guilty; but don't do it again."

What mattered was whether the prisoner who so escaped could take it—Madeleine could, and did.

*   *   *

Her departure from the court was achieved in the best cloak-and-dagger tradition in order to dodge the howling welcome outside, the plan being contrived by John Wilkie, the Glasgow end of the defence.

A young lady, a sort of Victorian bobby-soxer who vowed any payment in return for actually seeing and touching Miss Smith, was brought forward to don the idol's clothes, and

* The chronicler raised this point with a great advocate, now dead, when he ignored a client in court whose life he had just saved. The answer to this was: "Our job in defence is to free a client if possible; our private conclusions must remain our own."

off she went as a red herring for the crowd. Madeleine escaped by going out through the Advocate's Library with her brother Jack. They were whisked unmolested to the train and by ten o'clock that evening reached Rowaleyn, now alive again with human presence.

There is no news of how the family received her, but a faint clue exists in a letter to a "Miss Kemp." It is in a woman's handwriting and is both incomplete and anonymous. It refers to seeing "dear" James Smith for a moment on July 9, so "sad, so downcast my heart aches for him and his poor, stricken wife so ill and low." Perhaps, from this, the feelings at Rowaleyn may be judged. In that quiet house the stage had surely been reached where blame or recrimination was useless, and the depths of misery such that nothing would alter it for the moment.

Madeleine's nerve and spirits did not desert her. On every tongue her name might be, and, properly, she was a woman who might have taken to her bed or a nunnery—she showed no signs of it, but got down at once to her bread-and-butter letters.

From Miss Tennyson Jesse, who wrote the opening comment, comes a letter which is shown in her preface to *The Trial of Madeleine Smith*:

. . . Four days later she wrote a letter to Miss Aitken, the matron of Edinburgh prison, which is far more profoundly shocking than any of her violent epistles to L'Angelier:

Dear Miss Aitken. You shall be glad to hear I am well—in fact I am quite well, and my spirits not in the least down. I left Edinburgh and went to Slateford, and got home to Rowaleyn during the night. But alas I found Mama in a bad state of health. But I trust in a short time all will be well with her. The others are all well. The feeling in the west is not so good towards me as you kind Edinburgh people showed me. I rather think it shall be necessary for me to leave Scotland for a few months, but Mama is so unwell we do not like to fix anything at present. If you ever see Mr C. Combe tell him that the panel was not at all pleased with the verdict. I was delighted with the loud cheer the court gave. I did not feel in the least put about when the jury were out considering whether they should send me home or keep me. I think I must have had several hundred letters all from gentlemen some offering me consolation and some their hearths and homes. My *friend* I know nothing of—I have not seen him. I hear he has been ill, which I dont much care. I hope you will give me a note. Thank Miss Bell and Agnes in my name for all their kindness and attention to me. I should like you to send me my Bible and watch to 124, St. Vincent Street, Glasgow to J. Smith. The country is looking most lovely. As soon as I know my arrangements I shall let you know where I am to be sent to. With kind love to yourself and Mr Smith ever believe me, yours sincerely

MADELEINE SMITH.

There, in that off-hand dismissal, was the epitaph of faithful William Minnoch. He did not appear to take it too much to heart, for, later, he married well, became a comparatively wealthy man and the much respected chairman of the Glasgow Chamber of Commerce.

Meanwhile Scotland, through its newspapers, had a great deal to say, even more than before the trial; England did as well. In Jersey an English-language paper devoted a unique special edition to a full report of the whole court proceedings. There was a comment on the usual last minute witness, someone who had seen a man (in dress similar to Emile's) and a woman on Sunday night, March 22, between twelve and one, uttering endearments in the lane at the back of 7 Blythswood Square.

The Times thought:

> The jury by their verdict have declared their inability to decide. In this verdict we must concur . . . Madeleine Smith goes free from the penalties of the law—and that is all.

The Saturday Review was more dramatic:

> She found that she had ventured everything on an unworthy object, and the very depth of her love was changed, on the complete and perfect sense of utter loss, into the corresponding depth of hatred . . .

The Examiner thought the verdict "will be generally approved", while *The Leader* did not see how the jury could have "come to any other decision." *The Scotsman* considered Madeleine "either the most fortunate of criminals or the most unfortunate of women."

A violent argument broke about the head of a minister whose pulpit comments aroused agreement or fury. The more sensational newspapers went interestedly into the cost of the trial, explaining how the defence had been paid by various kindly donations; it was, in fact, paid for by James Smith, a bill of £4,000—with his rigid principles any form of charity would have been the last thing he would have considered or accepted. The Dean of Faculty received £250, plus a morning refresher for each day of the trial. Even so, the total amount seems excessive but perhaps legal costs were as astronomical as they are today.

Emile's friends rallied to his side, praising him and producing many proofs of his character, including a pathetic letter from Melanie Langelier; she was, indeed, utterly grief-stricken and failed to recover from the melancholy of it all. She died in 1866. Elmire said she was never really ill "but declined slowly over the years and died, dear Mama, of a broken heart." There can be no reason to doubt it.

*   *   *

Madeleine continued to be the storm centre of a spate of discussion, particularly of pamphlets for and against her. The most savage of these was *The Story of Minie L'Angelier*, issued in Edinburgh in 1857, which decided "she cannot, even by the most singular advantages of suppressed evidence, and a most bewildering, impressive, and eloquent defence by her counsel, free herself from the charge of the most atrocious, premeditated and cold-blooded murder." There were similar comments, if less biting.

Dr. Christison, unlike the pathologist in the Maybrick case,* left no personal opinion, but there is a reliable anecdote about Inglis, the Dean of Faculty, who was asked, at a

* See *This Friendless Lady* (Frederick Muller).

private dinner, his *true* opinion of Madeleine's guilt. He satisfied himself with a cautious view that he would "sooner have danced than supped with her," and left it at that. One modern legal opinion of sound authority uttered on the case during the writing of this book was to the effect that Madeleine, whether she went into the witness box or not, would have been doomed had she been tried today.

The Smith family moved to Bridge of Allan and there remained for a time. Despite the seclusion in which they lived, there was obviously a feeling of being spied on, particularly while in the newspaper columns battles continued to rage as readers fought each other with letters.

James Smith bestirred himself enough to seek a new home, and found one at Old Polmont, just off the Stirling–Edinburgh road.

It was the house where he was to live for a few years, Polmont Bank, a large, square building in solid Victorian style, built of local stone. In an acre of partially wooded garden, facing the main village street, he had a fine view from his front windows to the Orchil Hills; in the years of peace he characteristically designed and built a dining-room wing on to his home.

He died there very soon after, in 1863, leaving £3,000 to each of his children with the exception of Madeleine, whose trial he had paid for and to whom he made a handsome present on her marriage. Mrs. Smith died shortly afterwards, to be followed by Bessie. Jack remained in London, where he set up in his father's profession, while little James stayed in Scotland.

Janet, heir of her mother and sister, never married and spent the rest of her life in Falkirk, in a house called Bellevue. With two servants to look after her, she took some part in local charitable affairs.

Before all this happened, Madeleine went to London with her brother, Jack, and there began to enjoy a comfortable life which, for her, still held many years of interest and change.

* * *

It was at a small tea in her flat in Sloane Street she met an amusing, remarkably charming twenty-four-year-old man named Wardle. He was brought by some friends from the quasi-artistic circles in which Madeleine was now mixing, for the change in the world and the rapid realignment of intellectual research intrigued her.

George Young Wardle was clever and original, a draughtsman of great ability, and a mediaevalist and antiquary who was also something of a fiery thinker. It was inevitable that he was to become part of William Morris's circle.

He met Madeleine both at her flat, and in Glasgow where he went, with his brother Thomas, to inquire into the lost art of indigo dyeing. Wardle later became Morris's manager at the Queen Square establishment, but first pressed his suit on Madeleine, and won her.

They were married in Knightsbridge on July 4, 1861. James Smith must have breathed in relief when his problem child decided to settle down at last—even if, in all likelihood, he may not have approved of her choice—but he attended the wedding, and the reception held that evening in Regent Street, and dowered her generously as a nuptial gift. There is no other news of the event than this, and that "many artists and their friends were present"; this, too, cannot have pleased James Smith—it could be that he was past fighting the inevitable any more.

Madeleine took admirably to domesticity, living in a small Bloomsbury Street house where, with her charm and intelligence, she became a well-liked hostess. She was a vivacious conversationalist, and given to forthright ideas she did not hesitate to express. She also took up something Emile had urged on her (which her mother would never hear of), and went in for water-colours. One demure little seaside scene, signed "M. H. Wardle," hangs in a Chelsea house to-day, given to its owner's grandfather by Mrs. Wardle's own hands.

There were two children of the marriage, Tom, who was born six years later, and a girl (known as "Kitten") soon after that. In their early years they were little seen. It has been reported that Wardle's son, Tom, was tried for making Socialist speeches in Edgware Road in 1886, a generally accepted error. It is worth correction, for accuracy's sake. The Tom Wardle concerned was the son of (Sir) Thomas Wardle, of Leek, who lived near his Uncle George. He was a political agitator with original ideas, who, when he was thirty-five in 1886, was tried for obstructing the highway by making a public speech, and for arguing with a policeman. The court forgave such youthful impetuosity and bound him over; he got a severe dressing down from George, a vigorous letter objecting not so much to his political beliefs but to his manner of spreading them: "Say what you think, my dear boy, but do, at least, preserve the peace whilst doing so" is his conclusion to a paternal and kindly reprimand.

By 1883 Wardle was making over £1,000 a year at William Morris and Company, but the association did not continue much longer—by 1889 he had resigned and was going his own way, a staunch individualist whose original mind was superficially expressed by a taste for original clothes, giving him the appearance of a latter day Augustus John.

All was not well between him and Madeleine. Their outlooks and tastes became more and more incompatible until the marriage slowly but surely failed. Before long they had separated amicably and for mutual comfort. Madeleine stayed in London for the time being, but Wardle went off to Italy,* something he had wanted to do for years, staying there until he finally decided to return and live in Fowey, Cornwall —he died in a nursing home at Plymouth in 1910 of cancer, without having had any contact with his wife for some years.

Madeleine's vitality was undiminished. Her children were no longer with her (the son had gone to live in the United

* The late Gilbert Murray is the reliable authority for a statement, hitherto undivulged, that he met George Wardle in Italy "in hiding." It appears Wardle had "seen a look" in Madeleine's eyes which so alarmed him that he fled. It must have been a clear and convincing look, pregnant with meaning, for Wardle was never an alarmist.

States), and she wanted company, preferably different company. She departed to live at Leek, close to her brother-in-law, Sir Thomas Wardle, but not, as has been written in other books, on his bounty. They had always been good friends.

Her means were small but sufficient. She was also in the best of health, filled with energy but, as the years went on, none too pleased in the way the great case continued to appear time after time in print. This was particularly so when a clerk in the Justiciary Office at Edinburgh abstracted and sold a number of the original documents from court files. He went to prison for a year, and once more Madeleine Smith's name was noisily publicised.

From time to time Madeleine "died." She had, and the report is still regularly re-published, married a surgeon named Tudor Hora and died in Australia; she also "met her death" in the United States, and in France. According to many newspapers, magazines, and quite a few criminological writers, her deaths in the nineteenth century, and the beginning of the twentieth, are remarkable in their variety and originality.

It is possible she rejoiced in these as indicating attention was being directed away from her. What she did was to try to shield herself and, as Henry James wrote in a letter to William Roughead:* ". . . she precisely *didn't* squalidly suffer, but lived on to admire, with the rest of us, for so many years, the rare work of art with which she had been the means of enriching humanity."

What she did do was to preserve her anonymity as when, during the days at Leek, she visited Janet in Falkirk for a fortnight as "Mrs. Lena Wardle"—she had long adopted the disliked diminutive bestowed on her by Bessie so many years ago.

When Sir Thomas Wardle died, she was alone once more. She stayed for a while with a woman friend and she, too, died.

In the reign of Edward VII Madeleine was flourishing—

* *Tales of the Criminous.*

tough, undiminished, and filled with life.* She had no time for weakness, and never did have. Instead of settling down with her small means to a tranquil existence, she suddenly tired of her world. Her son was in the United States (where she had visited him several times) and Madeleine decided abruptly she would go there, about two years before George Wardle's death.

Unlike the wishful thinkers in the aftermath of the trial who could swear to having "seen" Madeleine Smith leaving for the United States, she really did so this time, departing from her native soil where most of her contemporaries had died, even if she was 'unforgotten and never would be forgotten.

* There is a story still quoted that about this time she met the late H. B. Irving and was asked by him, if history were to repeat itself, if she would have acted just as she had in the past. Her answer was an affirmative. In view of her care in keeping her own counsel, the chronicler has never felt this anecdote can be wholly accurate.

CHAPTER SIXTEEN

And Madeleine Smith?

As an amateur of the case, I have pondered its mysteries
for years. Did she? Yes; can you think otherwise?

E. Powys Mathers (*"Torquemada"*).*

IN THE UNITED STATES there was a new happiness for Madeleine, a place where she was exposed to new ideas. The strings tieing her to home and to memories were cut, perhaps for ever.

But not entirely so. The case was too big, too fascinating for it to die. The story, having endured for so long, was again and again revived, figuring in book after book retelling the details of ancient murders. Now and then pamphlets would be published; at private discussions the case often got an airing. People would not forget Madeleine Smith and gradually there grew up a mass of misinformation, of legend, of distorted fact, much of which prevails today.

Mrs. Lena Wardle was not interested. The past was dead in her eyes. She went out of her way to keep it buried. Despite suggestions and reports, supposedly from her lips, she never allowed the case to get any comments from her.

She was really happy for the first time in her life, in the sense of being free, with nothing to hold her down. She blossomed as a personality in her own right, unafraid gracious, and intelligent with the wisdom of the increasing years.

Youth seemed her permanent possession. She took full advantage of it, and to deflect any possible coincidence, were it ever to come out, she lopped years away from her

* In a private letter.

188

age and let them stay forgotten. With her looks she could easily maintain the harmless fiction.

Somewhere in her progress she met a man named Sheehy, younger than she was, a kind, gentle, friendly soul who admired her. She grasped the promise of a last happiness, and married him.

But she remained her strong-minded self. Sheehy was a Roman Catholic; this she accepted, remaining true to her, own faith, never to depart from it. Her husband was too easy-going to raise any objections—it would have been all the same if he had done so, for she was Madeleine Smith.

In the later part of her married life they moved to New York City, to exist quietly and in content. They saw the first world war pass by, to leave them unscathed. Their wants were few and their joint means sufficient. Sheehy supported his wife in comfort while she saved her own income for what she called her "old age," funds which came largely from home, including the rents of several houses and tenements she owned.

When she was nearly ninety it seemed as if she was no more than sixty (and, officially, she passed as it). She was stouter, what her father's generation would have called "the fine figure of a woman," and she moved well if majestically. She was scrupulous about her personal appearance, and a faddist for impeccable grooming.

Her hair was abundant. Discreetly rouged and made up, she looked vital and was vital, attracting all beholders. They always paid her attention.

That curious magnetism and animation never left her, that compelling sex appeal which could not be resisted. When she entered a restaurant in her last years, she was a target for the curious. People liked her on sight, talking to her wherever she went, finding her conversational powers outstanding. Well read, well informed, and well balanced, Madeleine could interest anyone.

She was Lena Wardle Sheehy to her friends. Any callers at her apartment were always welcome, and there she would sit, entertaining and fascinating them. To the end her eyes were perfect; she never had any need for glasses. Nor did she depend on ready-made clothing; she had learned in an old-fashioned school to make all her own clothes, and continued to do so, down to the dress she completed a few days before her death and in which she was buried.

Madeleine was deeply grieved when her second husband died unexpectedly, and was laid to rest as he desired in St. Raymond's Cemetery,* Bronx. This time she was not alone; there were relatives and friends, people who were devoted to her. But the world had not entirely finished with her.

In the New York *Sunday Chronicle*, on April 3, 1927, there appeared a most disturbing story:

> At a moment when she is almost on the brink of the grave a woman has been served by the American authorities a notice on the grounds that she may become a charge on public funds.
>
> Despite her desire for retirement, Madeleine Smith, the central figure in one of the most sensational poison dramas of the last century, has now been forced into the limelight again through the action of the United States authorities in serving her with a notice to quit America within one month on the plea that she is in danger of becoming a charge on public funds.
>
> It is many years now since Madeleine Smith left London, where she was attached to the Socialist Movement, to settle in the United States in the hope that she could live down memories of the terrible drama with which she was associated.
>
> Until quite recently she was living in an assumed name in a small town in the Middle West.
>
> Her story is that she would have been left in peace but for the fact that on her refusal to come out of retirement to take part in a film dealing with the drama in which she figured, her name and past were broadcast by the Press with the result that Washington has been petitioned to deport her.
>
> The case in which Madeleine Smith figured excited interest throughout the whole world . . .

---

* This will be familiar to the informed reader, for it was outside the wall, one dark night a few years later, that Dr. Condon met the kidnapper of the Lindbergh baby and there handed over the fifty thousand dollar ransom to Hauptmann, while Colonel Lindbergh waited near by.

"I have been acquitted of the murder charge and I claim that people have no right to persecute me further," Madeleine Smith told me today. "Surely an old woman of 90 may be allowed to end her days in peace without having the past raked up against her.

"I deny that I am ever likely to become a charge on public funds in America or any other country, and all I ask is to be left to end my days in peace. It is said that I should return to my native Scotland, but my answer is that I cannot bear to return to a land that has such bitter memories for me."

Though she herself is a Presbyterian, Miss Smith has arranged for Masses to be said for the repose of the soul of the lover she was accused of killing, and these have been said at her expense for nearly 60 years.

This unwanted publicity, so close on Sheehy's death, and a year before her own, made Madeleine unhappy.

But it is difficult to understand how the contretemps could have arisen at all.

There *was* an attempt to get her—with Hollywood's usual complete lack of good taste—to take part in a film of her own life, but it came to nothing when she would have no part of it. And it is quite possible some word did reach Washington, in typical garbled Hollywood form, about her on which some action was taken.

But if it was ever more than a formality, it was quickly scotched, for Madeleine never lacked for money and the suggestion she would become a public charge was no more than wishful official thinking without verification of facts. Not only was she able to produce ample proof of means, but her marriage to Sheehy obviously made her a citizen.

Yet the newspaper report was of the quality which so often tagged her later life. The only assumed name she used was her own, and she certainly did not live in the Middle West. Why an old bromide about L'Angelier, the story of the Masses, should be brought up again is also difficult to understand. He was not only a Protestant in his last years, is buried in a Protestant church, but that she should have ordered such Masses sounds not only unlike her, but something she would never have done when L'Angelier himself, in the past, had made it clear in which direction his religious sympathies lay.

It has been suggested, and this seems most reasonable, that the real truth behind the unwelcome intrusion into her peace was that she had once been associated, casual though that association was, with the Socialist Movement. As, in 1927, the United States was undergoing one of its recurrent outbreaks of hysteria against certain political beliefs (Sacco and Vanzetti were executed that same summer), the answer to the reason for putting the Government's eyes on her may have been through some spiteful unknown's action.

The point can be cleared up in a brief aside. Madeleine's sympathies were never particularly Socialistic; she was interested in the days of her marriage to Wardle because so many of her intellectual friends were finding in Socialism the panacea for all ills. She shared their enthusiasm with some detachment, but willingly helped when she could because she genuinely enjoyed helping people.

For a short time, in 1887, she acted as a temporary treasurer to a "cell" of the Socialist League, its chairman being Edward Aveling, son-in-law of Karl Marx. She not only did this but at one time did some work for another pink organisation, known as the Central Democratic Club, but her views, while forthrightly "modern" at all times, usually inclined to preference for a stabilised form of society and once, anyway, she referred to friends with advanced views whom she considered "amusing visionaries"—it possibly sums her real feelings.

Her daughter, Kitten, has been noted as approving Ibsen and free love, this second a most discourteous reflection on a young woman whose views were actually most healthily normal, and, which may have distressed her advanced friends, somewhat conventional.

But nothing was spared in Madeleine's life. It has become an article of faith that she wore a henna wig, a woman who was proud to the day of her death of her naturally profuse dark hair. It has also been suggested that she was a schizophrenic. This belief was fostered by her behaviour at the trial and other factors—a belief, in view of her history as it has now been uncovered, that is perhaps one of the wildest suggestions which could apply to her.

* * *

The last days had come now. She had been born into a world so different from the one she was living in, but had at least met it on its own terms by keeping up with it, dwelling contentedly in the most modern and noisiest of the earth's cities.

In her apartment on Park Avenue, Bronx, she was in the heart of a bewildering Americana. From the upstairs windows of the old building, drab in its fading dignity, she could see the sunken tracks of the New York Central Railroad parallel with the street. Below was the colour and movement of the Bronx—a delicatessen flanked her on one side and a Coca-Cola plant on the other. The dim age of Victoria in all its strangeness walked side by side with the rowdy complications of current life and tastes.

Her great span of years ended quietly on April 12, 1928, when she was stricken with kidney disease, and was taken to the graveyard of her choice, Mount Hope Cemetery, set in the lovely hills of Westchester County, some miles from New York City.

At first a plain marker was on her grave, bearing only a number (an ironic note, for had the jury decided against her, she would have lain under a prison number in permanent anonymity). But Madeleine had not overlooked the future, and had ear-marked certain money to buy her a proper stone.

Just two years before the centenary of the case, in 1955, the new stone was placed into position, of plain Barre Granite, bearing only that diminutive given by Bessie, and the name of the second husband.

She needed no more. Lena Sheehy can rest, her name blend and blur with the weather of the years. The woman beneath the stone will live on; the minds of men have never forgotten her and perhaps never will.

*　　*　　*

And was this woman of stout heart and firm purpose guilty? So many have debated the question and judged it, just as many will again. The fascination of it cannot be denied.

Personal opinion, whether it is right or wrong, must enter on the scene at the end of this book, a book more fully amplified than has previously been possible. It contains much that is new, and in the early chapters the hitherto quite unknown early days of both the protagonists must in some respects help to see them with readjusted vision. The child may not necessarily be the father of the man, but in his childhood must be indications of his future being, the foundation of his person and qualities as they were, and as they emerge in the stresses and strains of grown-up existence.

It is quite impossible to subscribe to the belief of Edgar Lustgarten that Emile L'Angelier was "also a born blackmailer, and of a type even more contemptible than most," nor can Miss Tennyson Jesse's judgment be accepted in that he was a "scheming, sensual, iron-willed lady-killer." More to the point is Lord Moncreiff's opinion in that 1906 number of *Blackwood's Magazine*: "He was not a blackmailer but anxious to prevent Madeleine from marrying Minnoch."

The frustrated lover, hysterically taking every foolish step without really meaning it, is so readily seen as a blackmailer and a rascal. This cast-off lover is often ugly in his behaviour because he acts without reason, impelled by the possible loss of his girl. It is biology in action, not a projection of the conscious mind; it is the unthinking, greedy child who attacks viciously to hold what he believes or regards as his own. Time takes care of it as time would have taken care of Emile.

That he might have gone to James Smith with the letters cannot be denied. It was a perfectly natural thing for one in

his state of mind to do, but not out of evil. In the weak any
trick can serve to save the day. If his loved one would not
come willingly to his bed and if he could not have her, then
he determined no other man should have that pleasure.

He might *not* have gone with the letters. He might, like so
many of the young, have uttered his threats and promised
theatrical forms of retribution; he might even have killed
himself later on. But the curious resiliency of human nature,
and the healing process of time in its flight, were certain
palliatives. Filled with agony, self-pity, and a sense of loss,
the lover is a mad creature—at times he will act in a way he
will always regret; in other moments a last shred of good
sense holds him back. Time is, therefore, the essential requirement. Emile never had it.

The question of the poisoning and debates on whether or
not it could be taken without detection needs little attention.
That larger doses than 82 grains can be unknowingly absorbed
can be qualified, for example, by the case of a woman named
Alice Holt, who was executed in 1863 at Chester for the
murder of her mother with arsenic (and certified, at the time,
by the family physician as gastro-enteritis). No less than
154 grains were found in the dead woman's stomach; the
actual dose must have been enormous. It was undetected in
the taking.

The fact of suspension in liquid and consequent lack of
awareness by the victim has been shown. Most, if not all,
that debated large dose could have been dissolved in cocoa
and there need not necessarily have been any taste. It might
have been a trifle bitter but sense of taste is variable, and
sugar deceives the tongue—too much sugar can taste bitter,
as well.

The soot, were it adulterated arsenic, may have caused
discolouration. It would not have been remarkably obvious,
and not obvious at all if the liquid had been drunk in semi-
darkness. Dissolving the poison in water beforehand, for
example, would have allowed the soot to sediment and using
the supernatant fluid would have covered this with the help

of cocoa. The arsenic must have been in the main body of the drink, and, in any case, people seldom drink cocoa to the dregs.

The degree of throat burning has always been discussed, but, like everything else, depends on personal idiosyncrasy. If Emile had indeed been a laudanum taker, this factor alone could have contributed to lessening to some extent the "feel" of burning. But plain simplicity of everyday behaviour is probably the real answer.

Perhaps in the semi-darkness, sipping hot, sweet cocoa, or even coffee, and with his loved one at his side, would Emile have paid particular attention to his drink? Had it been laced with vast quantities of arsenic, and he had drunk a little of it, he would have absorbed enough for the purpose in hand.

And there is the atmosphere. Would it not be, were a poisoner controlling the scene, one of simple staging? There could have been charm and fondness on the part of the drink's giver, for the purpose of covering up. Emile, in ecstasy at the promise of the future, would have drunk innocently, a besotted male largely unaware if he was drinking cocoa or straight whisky. Sipping it dutifully—hot, sweet, and cloying—he would have had his eyes and his entire attention on Madeleine, not determining the degree of taste in his drink.

The victim does not usually begin uttering cries from a page in a book on medical jurisprudence, stating that his mucous membranes are being unusually irritated and he is aware of a precise degree of throat burning, nor does he point out that the sedimentary base is formed of gritty particles which are setting up focal points of discomfort in his gums—if he is with his sweetheart, he probably says the drink is too sweet or bitter or what the devil is in it—arsenic, or something? But he goes on sipping quickly, and is only too anxious to please her by getting down some of the drink and his arms around her again.

Academic theories as to why the victim took the drink

and why did he fail to remark on it or detect in it this and that are pointless. Moments of love run circles round exact physical reactions to dangerous intake, or the text-book *feelings* to be found in poisons—a passionate, waiting female can disguise something curious in drink or food better than anything in the pharmacopoeia.

What Emile would have noticed and what he did not notice are of considerably less importance than *whether* Madeleine poisoned him. The arsenic was in his stomach and it killed him—the reations of his taste-buds, or the lack of those reactions, are immaterial.

*   *   *

The law's three counts can be boiled down to the one: attempts at murder, if such they were, or try-outs, again if such they were, are also immaterial compared with the final result of accomplished murder.

The letter summoning Emile from Bridge of Allan has been comprehensively dealt with and must stand for what it was—an assignation for Sunday night, which he kept.

Would she poison him, and did she? She had the motive; she appears to have had the opportunity, and she certainly had the poison.

She had sinned. A young girl had given her passionate love to a young man, breaking all the rules laid down for her, and in a day when they were strictly enforced.

For a time he was her whole life. His touch made her happy and to see him for a moment was delight. He was her husband as she was his wife, at first in thought, and later in deed in the sight of God and by the physical rules of men.

There are two distinct possibilities. When she tired of him and chose Minnoch, there is Miss Tennyson Jesse's contention that "the woman who murders her husband has nearly always ceased to think of him as such" and therefore objects to his very existence when she wishes to take another. The "old" husband threatens "the beautiful little fairy castle she has built up for herself and her new lover." She wishes to remove the impediment both from her own consciousness and "also from the consciousness of others."

It may well be, but using this contention for the Madeleine Smith case (for which it was not intended) is to strain at probability. It may also be attributing to Madeleine a depth of thought and feeling foreign to the nature she has revealed.

In personal judgment, once more, some points have not been clarified to the extent necessary for the proposition of her innocence or guilt.

When Minnoch came into the picture, and she wished to be free of Emile, she may have calculated the question of the letters she could not recover. She had, as has been said, sinned, but who would be made aware of that sin? The main parties were her family and her new lover.

Parents are notorious for their readiness to forgive sin; the greater it is the greater the degree of forgiveness, if the repentance is sincere. To them Madeleine would have been shown as a stupid, misguided, and wicked girl. She had been bewitched and seduced, but she was still a girl. She was the eldest child of her parents, and love can be a mighty source of pity; that she had broken certain sacred rules may not entirely have counted. The Victorians, stern as they were, had a strong sense of justice. James Smith's rage at the facts in the letters could have been subjected to two things, with a third in the running.

Madeleine had done what she had done, but she was truly repentant when—to continue the surmise—the facts came out; Minnoch was there, and Smith loved his child in his own way. In fiction it is easy and dramatic to cast off the wanton; in life many things interfere. At least one of them would have been the reaction of the outside world, the omnipotent "they"—kept within the family, Madeleine's sin was only that. Cast off, and it could come out; "they" would have heard, judged, and spoken aloud.

There was William Minnoch, a good and decent man. He loved her and was some years her senior. His depth of character was such that great forgiveness could not have been beyond it. A good man often forgives the woman he loves, and overlooks her past, even the worst of it. Minnoch may not have done this, yet it was not beyond him; it is not over-simplification but the realisation that human nature is invariably capable of fine gestures when it is helped by sanity and understanding.

The letters in Madeleine's considerations, with the possibilities as to her parents and Minnoch, may have thus been analysed. They could have been less important than she made them out to be, and as people have since believed. Abandoning her naturally hysterical reactions, she possibly assayed the factors on *her* side in the knowledge that, shorn of drama, they did not necessarily mean the end of everything.

In the precision of detached cogitations, and her weighing of the problem, her excellent mind must surely have judged things carefully, seeing the letters in proper perspective. And she must have come up against a much more formidable problem, the consummated marriage between herself and Emile.

As a prior parallel to a state of mind, and to illuminate the reader who is not a Scot, there is a famous law case.

This is *Leslie* v. *Leslie* where a Divinity student formed an attachment for his landlady's daughter at a date prior to 1840.

They corresponded for many years, but before this he obtained a parish and joined the Scottish Ministers' Widows' Fund as a bachelor. In the letters the pair addressed each other as "husband" and "wife" though the "marriage" was never consummated.

In one way or another he put off the actual ceremony of marriage, and it never took place. When he died, after forty years of procrastination due to things like a "lack of funds," "proper furniture" and so on, the landlady's daughter claimed the amount due, payable by the Widows' Fund, as if she were really the dead man's wife.

It was held in court by *consensus de presenti* that she had indeed been his wife, consent alone being sufficient. She got the money.

Now Madeleine knew the customs of her country rather better than L'Angelier (and could she not, possibly, have read of the famous Leslie case at some time?), and maybe feared Emile in her heart as a stumbling block not so much because of the letters he refused to return, but because if she married Minnoch he could, if he really wished to be difficult, go after her for a form of bigamy.

If she wed Minnoch and Emile raised objections, he could have had this marriage nullified in getting the irregular union declared by court decree. The legal pros and cons are of small matter; what can have counted was Madeleine's knowledge that she was not trying to get rid of a lover who held letters against her which could make *private* trouble, but a *husband* who could no doubt get his legal standing settled in open court.

* * *

It was a very different matter indeed, and it is only belittling Madeleine's intelligence not to suppose such a thing could have counted in her mind above all else.

Those letters, dozens of them, to my "husband," so many talking of the marriage in spirit, of the consummation, and the signature, "Mimi L'Angelier"—she had woven a difficult net to escape from. This could have troubled her far more than the impact effect of the letters on her kin and her fiancé.

Emile was a constant danger, even if he agreed to go peaceably away. He would not give up the letters and perhaps would not really make use of them when he calmed down, but she could never tell with him. Some time, some day his uneven temperament might suddenly have impelled him to go back on his promise and come into the open, demanding his own. A little thing could trigger it off—seeing her with her new husband; a baby; a chance remark, some unsuspected factor which would have blown away Emile's good resolutions and turned him into a husband wishing for his wife, and asking the law to see that he got her.

To Madeleine sin and forgiveness within her private circle

was one thing, but public blazoning of the marriage by declaration between her and Emile was very terrible indeed. Her family and Minnoch would be dragged into it; the world would have had the spectacle of a sorry scandal, and made a great deal of it. Escutcheon and public standing were words of reality to the Victorians; they counted for almost as much as life itself.

Murder is a means to an end. To plan it calls for care and initiative, but it is usually seen as an answer, a double line beneath an addition, to close it. The victim is dead and the great problem solved; the sun may come up and the clouds are permanently dispersed.

Madeleine faced an impasse which, even if Emile promised to make no unkind move, was always there. He was the danger, not the letters; the only way must surely have been the obvious one.

She would not have worked out the problem so precisely, but, reduced to plain terms, the bewildering untidiness of the human mind aims at such black and white definitions, even if it does not express them so clearly. If she had committed one of the worst sins, according to what men have said God ordained, and which men have definitely ordained, the subsequent state of panic cannot find transmission from one sin to the worst sin of all very difficult. The law is fond of regarding adultery and murder as close to one another; it really means that readiness to perform the first makes the second very much easier. It can be a matter of degree.

The death of Emile removed a source of real danger. He was a man who went down under illness from time to time. A final one would not have been unduly surprising. He had died, poor Emile, and, his friends would say, that was that. There need have been no reason to suppose his letters would be scrutinised, any more than the rest of his belongings; perhaps they would go to his family, perhaps they would be returned to Madeleine, or simply thrown away.

On any of these she could have counted. The things which belong to the dead, particularly when they are poor bachelors living in boarding-houses, are not necessarily examined for dark secrets. If the Langeliers had got the letters, or read them, she had no reason to imagine anything would come of it.

Death was an end, and with the burial of Emile would be interred the past. Madeleine would have known that people, ordinary decent people, do not go rushing to a man's girl friend, or to her parents, with cries denouncing a tale of illicit love.

At the assignation there were no onlookers, just as there never had been onlookers at less eventful meetings. He would have gone home after it, been unwell, and died. It was dangerous, as all murder is dangerous. The greatest danger of all was unimagined—that within the mind of the killer, who invariably believes the dead are tidily buried and no man asks questions. If murderers thought beyond the commission of the deed, other than in its advantages, the deterrent value would be far greater than any question of whether or not capital punishment can stay the killer's hand.

Madeleine could have conceived her crime deftly and well. Her mentality was capable of such planning, and there were no particular difficulties. The long story of deceit and furtiveness was ready-made as an ally. She was frank in her purchase, and had no reason to be otherwise. Why, she can have reasoned, would the buying of arsenic for rats be in any way connected with Emile's death from one of his attacks? In that state of mind can be the answer.

She was up against a real danger, the danger not of a lover's threats but what he could do in cold-blooded sanity at some later stage.

Emile had to go and go he did. To picture Madeleine as a sweet young girl with no wrong thoughts, or Emile as a good or bad man, seem beside the point in the matter of the deed. Murders have been committed for many reasons, some too trivial for belief, but the murderer's reasons have been sufficient unto himself. When people are placed in certain helpless positions, they react according to their characters;

their self-justification is inexplicable, even to themselves. A man does what he thinks is right or necessary—he poses a question and settles it to his satisfaction. If the world is out of step with him, it is the world's fault.

Reason suggests Madeleine committed murder. The facts appear to support it. The personal findings seem to be a possible answer because "they" and the fear of them is more powerful than other evils.

Safety is the most powerful need of all. If Caesar's wife is to be above suspicion, she must make sure the cause of it is removed.

Chronology

1823   Emile L'Angelier born in Jersey.
1835   Madeleine Smith born in Glasgow.
1842   L'Angelier's move to Edinburgh.
1852   (September)   He joins Huggins & Company, Glasgow.
1855   (March)   L'Angelier introduced to Madeleine.
        („)   Her first letter to him.
        (April)   Her first attempt to end association.
        (July)   Her second attempt to end association.
        („)   They become secretly "engaged".
        They are "husband" and "wife" to each other.
1856   (May 6)   Madeleine becomes L'Angelier's mistress.
        (Autumn)   William Minnoch first at Rowaleyn.
        (November)   The Smiths move to Blythswood Square.
1857   (January 28)   Madeleine accepts Minnoch.
        (February 2)   Tries to break with L'Angelier.
        („)   They are reconciled.
        („)   Madeleine tries to buy prussic acid.
        („ 19)   L'Angelier sees Madeleine and is later taken ill.
        („ 21)   Madeleine buys arsenic from Murdoch.
        („ 22)   L'Angelier's second illness.
        (March 6)   Madeleine buys arsenic from Currie; goes to Bridge of Allan.
        („ 12)   Arranges date of wedding with Minnoch.
        („ 17)   She returns to Glasgow.
        („ 18)   Buys more arsenic from Currie.
        („ 19)   L'Angelier goes to Bridge of Allan.
        („ 20/21)   Her urgent letter asking L'Angelier to see her.
        („ 22)   L'Angelier returns to Glasgow.
        („ 23)   He dies of arsenical poisoning.
        („ 24)   Post-mortem examination.

1857 (March 26)   Madeleine flees to Rowaleyn.
     („   26)   L'Angelier interred.
     („   31)   Madeleine arrested.
     („   31)   L'Angelier exhumed.
     (June 30)   The trial.
     (July 9)   Trial ends.
1861 (July 4)   Madeleine's first marriage.
1928 (April 12)   Death of Madeleine Smith, in U.S.A.
1955 Stone erected above her grave.

APPENDIX I

Report by Drs. Thomson and Steven:

At the request of Messrs. W. B. Huggins & Co., of this city, we, the undersigned, made a *post-mortem* examination of the body of the late M. L'Angelier, at the house of Mrs. Jenkins, 11 Great Western Road, on the 24th March current, at noon, when the appearances were as follows: The body, dressed in grave clothes and coffined, viewed externally, presented nothing remarkable, except a tawny hue of the surface. The incision made on opening the belly and chest revealed a considerable deposit of sub-cutaneous fat. The heart appeared large for the individual, but not so large as, in our opinion, to amount to disease. Its surface presented, externally, some opaque patches, such as are frequently seen on this organ without giving rise to any symptoms. Its right cavities were filled with dak fluid blood. The lungs, the liver, and the spleen appeared quite healthy. The gall bladder was moderately full of bile, and contained no calculi. The stomach and intestines, externally, presented nothing abnormal. The stomach, being tied at both extremities, was removed from the body. Its contents, consisting of about half a pint of dark fluid resembling coffee, were poured into a clean bottle, and the organ itself was laid open along its great curvature. The mucous membrane, except for a slight extent at the lesser curvature, was then seen to be deeply injected with blood, presenting an appearance of dark-red mottling, and its substance was remarked to be soft, being easily torn by scratching with the finger-nail. The other organs of the abdomen were not examined. The appearance of the mucous membrane, taken in connection with the history as related to us by witnesses, being such as, in our opinion, justified a suspicion of death having resulted from poison, we considered it proper to preserve the stomach and its contents in a sealed bottle for further investigation by chemical analysis, should such be determined on. We, however, do not imply that, in our opinion, death may not have resulted from natural causes; as, for example, severe internal congestion, the effect of exposure to cold after much bodily fatigue, which we understand the deceased to have undergone. Before closing this report, which we make at the request of the procurator-fiscal for the county of Lanark, we beg to state that, having had no legal authority for making the *post-mortem* examination above detailed, we restricted our examination to the organs in which we thought we were likely to find something to account for the death. Given under our hands at Glasgow, the 28th day of March, 1857, on soul and conscience.

(Signed) HUGH THOMSON, M.D.
(,,) JAMES STEVEN, M.D.

APPENDIX II

Major parts of two separate reports by Dr. Penny:

I hereby certify that on Friday, the 27th of March last, Dr. Hugh Thomson, of Glasgow, delivered to me, at the Andersonian Institution, a glass bottle containing a stomach and a reddish-coloured turbid liquid, said to be the contents of the stomach. The bottle was securely closed and duly sealed, and the seal was unbroken.

In compliance with the request of William Hart, Esq., one of the Procurators-Fiscal for the Lower Ward of Lanarkshire, I have carefully analysed and chemically examined the said stomach and its contents, with a view to ascertain whether they contained any poisonous substance.

1. CONTENTS OF THE STOMACH

This liquid measured eight and a half ounces. On being allowed to repose it deposited a white powder, which was found on examination to possess the external characters and all the chemical properties peculiar to arsenious acid; that is, the common white arsenic of the shops. It consisted of hard, gritty, transparent, colourless, crystalline particles; it was soluble in boiling water, and readily dissolved in a solution of caustic potash; it was unchanged by sulphide of ammonium, and volatilised when heated on platina foil. Heated in a tube it gave a sparkling white sublimate which, under the microscope, was found to consist of octohedral crystals. Its aqueous solution afforded, with ammonio-nitrate of silver, ammonio-sulphate of copper, sulphuretted hydrogen, and bichromate of potash, the highly characteristic results that are produced by arsenious acid. On heating a portion of it in a small tube with black-flux, a brilliant ring of metallic arsenic was obtained with all its distinctive properties. Heated with dilute hydrochloric acid and a slip of copper-foil, a steel-grey coating was deposited on the copper, and this coating by further examination was proved to be metallic arsenic.

Another portion of the powder, on being treated with nitric acid, yielded a substance having the peculiar characters of arsenic acid. A small portion of the powder was also subjected to what is commonly known as "Marsh's process," and metallic arsenic was thus obtained, with all its peculiar physical and chemical properties.

These results show unequivocally that the said white powder was arsenious acid; that is, the preparation of arsenic which is usually sold in commerce, and administered or taken as a poison under the name of arsenic or oxide of arsenic.

* * *

1. SMALL INTESTINE AND ITS CONTENTS

The portion of small intestine contained a turbid and reddish-coloured liquid, which measured four ounces. On standing for several hours in a glass vessel this liquid deposited numerous and well-defined octohedral crystals, which, on being subjected to the usual chemical processes for the detection of arsenic, were found to be arsenious acid.

Arsenic was also detected in the small intestine.

2. LARGE INTESTINE

This organ yielded arsenic, but in less proportion than in the small intestine.

3. LIVER, BRAIN, AND HEART

Arsenic was separated from the liver, heart, and brain, but in much less proportion than from the small and large intestine.

4. LUNG

The lung gave only a slight indication of the presence of arsenic.

CONCLUSIONS

1. That the body of the deceased Pierre Emile L'Angelier contained arsenic.
2. That the arsenic must have been taken by or administered to him while living.

All this is true on soul and conscience.

(Signed) FREDERICK PENNY,
Professor of Chemistry.

APPENDIX III

Emile L'Angelier's "diary" complete and as written:

1857

Wed.   11 Feb. —Dined at Mr J. Mitchell's
                Saw M. @ 12 P.M.
                In C.H. Room

Thurs. 12 Feb. —Spent the Even @ Pat. Kennedy's
                Major Stuart and wife
                D. Jameson & family

Frid.   13 Feb. —Saw Mr Phillpot
                  ,, Mimi
                dined at 144 Renfrew St.

Sat.   14 Feb. —*a* letter from M.—
Sun.   15 Feb. —St. Judes
Mon. 16 Feb. —Wrote M.—
                Saw Mr Philpots

Tues. 17 Feb. —Dined @ 144 Renfrew St
Thurs. 19 Feb. —Saw Mimi
                a few moments
                was very ill during the night

Frid.   20 Feb. —Passed two pleasant hour
                with M. in the Drawing Room

Sat.   21 Feb. —don't feel well
                went to T. F. Kennedy's

Sun.   22 Feb. —Saw Mimi in Drawing Room
                Promised me French Bible
                Taken very ill

1857

Mon. 23 Feb. —rec'd a letter from Mrs L.
Tues. 24 Feb. —Wrote M.
Wed. 25 Feb. —M. wrote me.
Sat.   28 Feb. —Mimi wrote me.

Mon. 2 Mar.—Wrote M L—Miss R.
              Brown.

Tues. 3 Mar.—Memi wrote
              wrote Mimi
                Saw her in S.S.

Wed. 4 Mar.—rec a letter from Brown
              saw Mimi gave her a
              note and got one from her

Thurs. 5 Mar.—a letter from Brown
              saw Mimi gave her a note
              and rec'd one—saw Midsumer's dream

Frid.   6 Mar.—Mimi goes to B of A
Sat.   7 Mar.—went to the gardens

Mon.   9 Mar.—Tea @ 144 Renfrew Street.
Tues.   10 Mar.—Went to Edin
Wed.   11 Mar.—Mrs White 5 Buccleugh Street
                    Mrs Jones
                    M'Call
Thurs. 12 Mar.—saw M'Call
Frid.   13 Mar.—Diner—
Sat.   14 Mar.—Saw the Gallery of Paintings
                    Dine with M'Call

BIBLIOGRAPHY

(Items marked with a * contain treatments of the case.

Trial of Madeleine Smith (Notable British Trials), ed. F. Tennyson Jesse (1927).
Trial of Madeleine Smith (Notable Scottish Trials), ed. A. Duncan Smith (1905).
Trial of Miss Madeleine Smith, issued by *The Scotsman* (1857).
Trial of Miss Madeleine Smith, issued by D. Mathers (1857).
Full Report of the Trial, from *The Times*, Read & Co. (1857).
*Reports of Trials for Murder, G. Lathom Browne & C. G. Stewart (1883).
*Look Upon the Prisoner, A. H. M. Brice (1928).
*Poison Romance and Poison Mysteries, C. J. S. Thompson (1899).
*Poisons and Poisoners, C. J. S. Thompson (1931).
*A Century of Murder, John Rowland (1950).
*Annals of Crime, W. H. Williamson (1930).
*Murder and its Motives, F. Tennyson Jesse (1924).
*Mysteries of Police and Crime, Arthur Griffiths (1898).
*The Woman in the Case, Edgar Lustgarten (1955).
*Famous Trials of the Century, J. B. Atlay (1899).
*Mainly Murder, William Roughead (1937).
*Splendours and Miseries, Sacheverell Sitwell (1943).
*Studies in Black and Red, Joseph Forster (1896).
*Riddles of Crime, Elizabeth Villiers (1928).
*A Gallery of Rogues, Charles Kingston (1924).
**Noted Murder Mysteries, Philip Curtin (Mrs. Belloc Lowndes), (1914).
*Murder at Smutty Nose, Edmund Pearson (1927).
**Murders and Murder Trials, H. M. Walbrook (1932).
*Famous Trials, Lord Birkenhead (1932).
*Is Mrs. Maybrick Guilty? (Maybrick and Smith Cases Contrasted), "L.E.X." (1889).
Case of Madeleine Smith Re-examined, "Omricon" (John Newton) (1857).
Madeleine Tried at the Bar, "Historicus" (1858).
Poison for Rats, "Legist" (1858).
Who Killed L'Angelier? "Scrutator" (1857).
Madeleine Smith, Geoffrey L. Butler (1935).
The Madeleine Smith Affair, Peter Hunt (1950).
The Story of Minie L'Angelier, issued by D. Macphail (1857).
Letters of Miss Madeleine Smith, issued by Astor Steam Press, New York (1858).
*The Power of Poison, John Glaister (1954).
*Buchanan's Forensic Medicine, John E. W. MacFall (1925).
*Forensic Chemistry, A. Lucas (1921).
*Memoir of John Inglis, J. C. Watt (1893).

GENERAL REFERENCES

The Life of William Morris, J. W. Mackail (1899).
Life of Sir Robert Christison, His Sons (1885).
Forensic Medicine and Toxicology, Woodman and Tidy (1877).
Forensic Medicine, Sydney Smith (1955).
Medical Jurisprudence, John Glaister (1955).

211

Forensic Medicine, Keith Simpson (1952).
Poisons, Frank Bamford (1940).
Etc., etc.

PERIODICALS

Murder Tour of Scotland, Eric Ambler, *Holiday* (Sept. 1956).
Etc., etc.
Chronique de Jersey, 11 April, 1857 (*et sq.*).
Jersey Times, 14 April, 1957 (*et sqq.*).
Illustrated Times, 11 July, 1857 (and in book form issued by G. Vicker, 1857).
The Journal of Jurisprudence, August, 1857 (*et sq.*).
The Lancet, July/August, 1857 (*et sqq.*).
Edinburgh Medical Journal, August and December, 1857.
Gentleman's Magazine, August, 1857 (*et sq.*).
Macphail's Ecclesiastical Journal, August, 1857.
Blackwood's Magazine, June, 1906.
And many newspapers and magazines here and in the United States, France, Germany, and some other countries, all having general or minor references to the case and its aftermath.